Power for Prairie Plows

Power for Prairie Plows

by

Grant MacEwan

Western Producer Prairie Books
Saskatoon, Saskatchewan

Western Producer Prairie Books
Saskatoon, Saskatchewan

First hardcover edition 1971
First softcover edition 1979

Book design by V. M. Wolfe

Cover photos: front cover at Austin, Man., Thresherman's Reunion; back cover, Clydesdales pulling in a contest at Pion-Era, Saskatoon in the early 1960's. Photos by R. H. Macdonald.

Printed and bound in Canada
by Modern Press
Saskatoon, Saskatchewan

Western Producer Prairie Books publications are produced and manufactured in the middle of western Canada by a unique publishing venture owned by a group of prairie farmers who are members of Saskatchewan Wheat Pool. Our first book in 1954 was a reprint of a serial originally carried in *The Western Producer,* a weekly newspaper serving western Canadian farmers since 1923. We continue the tradition of providing enjoyable and informative reading for all Canadians.

Canadian Cataloguing in Publication Data

MacEwan, John W. Grant, 1902 -
Power for Prairie plows

Includes index.
ISBN 0-919306-32-2
ISBN 0-88833-014-6 pa.

1. Farm mechanization — Prairie Provinces. 2. Draft animals - Prairie Provinces. 3. Agriculture - Prairie Provinces - History.
I. Title.
S760.C2M32 631.3'7 C72-2895

FOREWORD

It was the element of change that made the Western Canadian story so rich and exciting. Trading posts became centers of population and industry, buffalo ranges became wheatfields, cart trails became highways, and primitive farming implements gave place to machines of most intricate design. The evolutionary changes in farm power and in field machinery embraced everything from hand tools like the spades and the flails used by the Selkirk settlers, to implements drawn by oxen, then horses, steam tractors, and finally, the sophisticated powerplants mounted on rubber tires seen in recent years.

Every step in the dramatic development of farm power was acted out on the prairie stage, and as must be very clear, farm power, in its many and changing forms, played a big part in converting the old fur and buffalo country to an area of good and progressive farms. It is a story which should be captured and presented, not only for agricultural people but for all Canadians. Fortunately, much of that story has been preserved in pictures, and the desire to present many of those pictures was one of the motivating reasons for undertaking this book.

The author offers his gratitude to the good and helpful people in the Legislative Library, the Provincial Archives and the Glenbow Library and Archives, all of whom he has been bothering for years, also to those friends who searched family albums for appropriate illustrations and contributed them for this production. Nor should he fail to acknowledge the interest and encouragement offered by R. H. Macdonald of *The Western Producer* and his assistance in gathering illustrations.

Grant MacEwan

Chapter

CONTENTS

Chapter 1

Power to Pull a Plow

IN THE MAD SCRAMBLE to obtain homesteads and make them productive, draft power was an urgent necessity. Until land was broken, cultivated, and planted, there could be no crop and no return from the new soil. The earliest homesteaders saw the thousands of square miles of prairie and parkland and wondered how they could convert portions of the great expanse to wheat fields.

Getting the homestead was generally easier and less costly than getting the power with which to work it. A ten-dollar fee was enough to establish a claim to the homestead quarter section, but the minimum number of horses or oxen required to break and work the land would cost several hundred dollars. Nor was cost the only problem; it happened very often that newcomers in a position to pay cash for draft animals were prevented from so doing because supply fell far short of demand.

The Pat Burns experience was fairly typical. Arriving at Winnipeg in the spring of 1878, the chubby young Irish-Canadian had more of energy than money and walked 160 miles to Tanner's Crossing—later Minnedosa—where he located and filed on a homestead quarter section. Having neither horses nor oxen, and lacking the funds with which to buy them, he set out promptly to walk back to Winnipeg where he hoped to obtain work. He secured work with the Canadian Pacific Railway and drew wages of twenty-five dollars per month for blasting rock east of Winnipeg. After working for a year, he had saved enough money to pay for a team of oxen, a wagon, and a walking plow. It was standard equipment for the man setting out to take up residence on a homestead. Those Pat Burns oxen, as sulky and obstinate as other members of their race, succeeded in making a double contribution to western industry. After serving as draft animals for several years, the two aging critters were slaughtered and their carcasses were used to start their owner in the meat business.

Settlers without power might appeal to neighbors who had horses or oxen. There could be mutual advantage in exchanging work. "Let me use my ax to clear some land for both of us," the man without horses or oxen would propose, "and then you with your power can break and disc some land for both of us."

It was not every district which was so fortunate as to have a Jack Morton to whom homesteaders without money could come for horses. This man, "the Robin Hood of the Prairies," was believed to have had close to 5,000 horses at one time. Like Robin Hood, he was suspected of "lifting" stock from his prosperous neighbors, but when a struggling homesteader came begging for horses or steers that would make oxen, Jack Morton would say: "Get a lariat and rope a couple or four and if you can't pay me, don't let it keep you awake." Many more homesteaders than the records will ever show obtained their start in farming through the generosity of the big and colorful rancher from Rosebud, Alberta.

Men needing power would settle for anything available at low cost. Progress, they knew, would be determined by their success in harnessing the necessary draft animals. Mechanical power was still too far in the future to be considered, and the choice had to be made between ox-power, horsepower, mulepower, and what men could do with their own hands.

The prairie Indians had very little to offer the power-needy settlers. The native tribesmen used horses for riding and both horses and dogs to pull their travois, but they did not cultivate and found no reason to place harness on their horses. The Indian was never overburdened by equipment, his only invention resembling a vehicle was that travois, which consisted of two sticks or poles supported where they

The Plains Indians used horses for riding and both horses and dogs to pull their travois, a vehicle consisting of two poles on which they carried bundles of buffalo skins and other belongings. These Indian women were ready to start on a journey from Macleod, Alberta, in 1895.

Doukhobor women on Saskatchewan land in 1899, pulling the plows themselves, guided by one of the men from the sect. They chose to be their own beasts of burden, as religious beliefs forbade the working of God's other creatures.

Saskatchewan Archives Photo

Photo from Sam Stoochnoff

crossed at the horse's withers and allowed to drag in such a way that a bundle of buffalo skins or a disabled squaw could be carried on them. Although the acquisition of horses completely changed Indian ways, the Indian stock was generally small and insufficient in numbers to be of more than minor importance in meeting the needs of settlers. Indeed, it was the opinion of some individuals on the frontier that the Indians stole more horses from the homesteaders than the homesteaders bought from the Indians.

The first cultivation by the Selkirk settlers beside the Red and Assiniboine rivers was accomplished with hand spades and hoes. It was not until 1824, a dozen years after the settlement was founded, that the colonists had a plow and used horses and oxen to pull it. Understandably, the cultivated plots were small. But it was not the only time that the muscle needed to break western ground for cropping was furnished by humans. Because of religious beliefs which forbade the working of God's other creatures, certain immigrant people chose to be their own beasts of burden. Even the use of leather for harness was forbidden in some instances. Doukhobors—some 7,000 of whom came from Russia in 1899 and settled near Swan River, Kamsack, and Prince Albert— hitched their own people to plows and other implements, and a few pictures survive to show the stoutly-built women pulling walking plows through heavy ground, each plow being guided by one of the men of the sect.

By one means or another, most homesteaders managed to obtain oxen or mules or horses when they had to have them and then worked them shockingly close to the limits of their strength. Too often, the overtaxed animals fell victims to disease and died. Swamp fever accounted for thousands of horse losses. Death may have been a blessed relief for the overworked brutes, but their passing left the bereaved homesteaders in positions of helplessness. Settlers knew the loss of horses or oxen would be disastrous, and family prayers took note. The concern must have been repeated many times: "Lord, take care of the members of this family and spare our horses from swamp fever and glanders and from the hands of thieving Indians."

For a mental picture of frustration and helplessness, one may try to imagine the plight of that family of immigrants from Kansas stranded by the loss of mules somewhere near Battleford in 1895. The misfortune was reported by William McLelland, who was driving a big band of horses from Red Deer to Winnipeg for sale purposes. The four mules with which the newcomers hoped to become established and upon which they depended for transportation had strayed away one night and been gone

Desperate for power to pull his plow, the pioneer often resorted to some weird-looking animal combinations to get the job done. A horse and bull might work together, and often if the pioneer had no horses at all, the family cow would be substituted.

The Selkirk settlers did not have horses or oxen in the earliest years of their settlement beside the Red and Assiniboine rivers. For the first difficult year, they tilled the soil with hand spades and hoes and harvested by hand as well.

for two weeks, leaving the immigrants on the cool and friendless Prairies with a cow, some chickens, and a wagon loaded with equipment. Food was almost exhausted and the travelers were despondent. It must have seemed like an answer to prayer when McLelland, before moving on, presented the ill-fated travelers with a piece of bacon, half a bag of flour, and four bronco horses.

Considering the extreme urgency of the pioneer's need for power, it was not surprising that some strange and weird-looking animal combinations appeared on fields and trails. Herd bulls and milk cows did not escape the indignity of work harness. A Saskatchewan homesteader who lost one of his two horses hitched himself to work alongside the survivor. Two horses and two oxen working together to pull a seed drill or binder was not an uncommon sight. And Sam Romer, of Haynes, Alberta, was one who relieved the farm power shortage by driving a buckskin pony and the family milk cow together for all the ordinary kinds of field work. Together, cow and pony hauled the wagon in summer and sleigh in winter. And at harvest time, Sam Romer co-operated with a neighbor who had two mules and thereby made up a four-animal team consisting of two mules, one horse, and one cow to pull the binder. Neighbors recalled seeing Sam Romer going to the village to get his mail and groceries, riding his cow.

National Grain Photo by F. J. S. Holmes

Chapter 2

"The Damned Oxen"

NOBODY ADMITTED to a fondness for oxen. Nobody wrote slushy songs about them. Nobody shouted: "An ox, an ox, my kingdom for an ox." In thoughtful moments, a homesteader might acknowledge a debt to those uninspiring brutes that did much of the heavy pioneer slugging but he could not bring himself to a demonstration of affection the way he might with horses. Instead of loving them, he cursed them and kept them busy. But hard work made no perceptible impression upon the flinty character of the oxen. Their demeanor was unchanged. Their means of revenge was in the skill with which they could display contempt for those who mastered them and kept them at work. They would yield to human direction, but at their own speed and with a cutting composure. If the ox were working or chewing his cud, neither a friendly pat nor a slap with a whip would change the rhythm. He might move an ear to dislodge a fly but refuse to turn an eyeball at the approach of his owner. "Save your compassion for your horses and girl friends," the old ox seemed to say; "sentiment won't make my work any lighter so let's forget it."

By general agreement, oxen represented the lowliest form of road or farm power, lower than broncos, lower than mules. But neither their lowly estate, nor their capacity for insulting humans by ignoring them, nor their failure in creating a favorable public image was enough to prevent widespread acceptance in the pioneer communities. Unfortunately, there remained nothing to show the exact population in those years when oxen outnumbered horses because census officials did not bother to separate working oxen from ordinary steers being raised for beef. There is no doubt, however, that oxen, for some years, constituted the primary source of power for both freighting and farming and deserved more recognition and gratitude than they received.

The fact is that oxen have a very long association with agriculture, longer than that of either horses or mules. Egyptians of 5,000 years ago were hitching oxen and plowing with them. The earliest means of hitching consisted simply of securing a rope to the animal's horns and tying the other end of it to a plow. As an advance upon that crude method, the ox driver strapped a wooden bar across the horns and connected it by ropes or traces to the load. From this arrangement it was but a short step to the familiar bow yoke which permitted the animal to carry the weight of the load on the heavy muscles of its neck. The horn yoke principle did not disappear, however, and can be seen in use today in the Canadian Maritime Provinces where oxen continue to find acceptance. A pair of Nova Scotia oxen is ready for work when the yoke is strapped to the horns, the chain connection between load and metal ring at the center of the yoke is in position, and the ox driver, with a chew of tobacco in his mouth and a short whip in his hand, takes his place at the animals' heads.

To the ancient Romans, the ox was both servant and companion, and commanded respect. In recognition of its varied services, the animal received the special favor of the goddess Ceres. And Cato (234 B.C. - 149 B.C.), who wrote extensively about farm management and shared the old Roman regard for oxen, had some advice for people who were buying and using them. The purchaser should select animals of three or four years in age, preferably those having deep chests, heavy quarters, and large black horns. In the case of pairs or teams, Cato said, the individuals should be matched for strength so that a relatively weak ox would not become worn out by a stronger mate.

In breaking oxen, according to Cato, the person undertaking the task should begin by fastening a single yoke to the animal and leaving it for several days. The next step would involve hitching or yoking the young ox with an older and more experienced one. After working together without a load, the pair would be ready for a light burden and finally for such heavy work as plowing. It was a technique which changed little through the years. Cato's advice about changing sides in an ox team might seem to be more strange; rather than driving an ox consistently on the same side in a team, reversing sides now and then for the relief that would come from change was desirable, according to the observant Roman.

Romans occupying Britain until the fifth century used

The Red River carts were a familiar sight on the Prairies in pre-railroad days. In 1860 travelers to Fort Garry, shown here in the background, depended on the Red River Ferry, but at most river crossings in the West they were on their own. Shallow streams could be forded easily because of the cart's high wheels, and at deeper crossings the wheels were removed and lashed under the cart, which would then be floated across.

Family Herald and Weekly Star Illustration

oxen for farming and drove them in pairs. For centuries following the Roman withdrawal, the favored size for an English farm was the amount of land a man could plow and cultivate with one pair of oxen. By the nineteenth century, four-ox teams and even six-ox teams were seen on English fields. Oxen were worth more for plowing than for beef, and owners displayed pride in them. There was no stigma attached to oxen or the men who used them.

Settlers along the St. Lawrence River and those who went into the bush of Upper Canada relied upon oxen to drag their firewood, pull their plows, haul hay from around the stumps, and when the animals were no longer serviceable, furnish carcasses of beef for winter rations. Oxen were logical choices, and in the New West, the advantages of work cattle were just as obvious.

Red River carts, those two-wheeled inventions which became popular across the West, were primarily oxcarts. It was not uncommon for horses to be used to pull them, but in the years when the long trains of a hundred or more carts moved slowly over the Fort Garry-St. Paul and Fort Garry-Fort Edmonton trails, most of the beasts of burden were oxen. The first Red River carts, "Pembina buggies," were made at Pembina, North Dakota, about 1801, and construction was entirely of wood except for the green buffalo skin wrapped around the wheel rims to serve as tires. Manitoba oak was favored for axles and elm for hubs. Their production became a Métis specialty. Wheels were never greased, the theory being that a lubricant would collect grit and wear the axles down. Hence the screaming sound of dry axles which could be heard for miles. Indians, hating the shrill noise, contended that it sent the buffalo into hiding in the skies.

In addition to some experience, to be a maker of Red River carts a man needed only an ax, an auger, a saw, a drawknife, and the necessary wood and green hide. And to be an ox driver on the long "trains," he needed patience. It was argued that a forceful vocabulary was also necessary, but it was doubtful if strong language made any real impression upon the staid cattle. Nobody could be sure if profanity was a prerequisite to driving or the inevitable by-product. In commanding the shattering language which was supposed to be typical of drivers or skinners, the men who directed the big "bull teams" hauling freight wagons on the Calgary-Fort Macleod-Fort Benton trail were the acknowledged masters. Their animals, it was argued, understood only the most violent expletives.

On a certain trip from Calgary to Fort Macleod, the ox driver had a parson for a passenger, and a few miles

Multiple teams of oxen, known as bull trains, moved much of the freight across the West before the days of the railroad, in all seasons of the year. A large train could consist of eighteen wagons in all and over 100 oxen.

Steele & Co. Photo

out of Calgary, the big wagons became stuck in the mud. Shouting to the oxen in restrained language achieved nothing. The wagons settled more deeply in the mud. The driver knew the reason for his difficulty and knew there was only one way to overcome it. Turning to his ecclesiastical passenger, he said: "Parson, I've got to swear."

"But," replied the minister, "if you swear, you won't get to Heaven."

Said the exasperated driver: "That's too bad. But if I don't swear, you'll never get to Fort Macleod."

The passenger agreed to plug his ears. The driver delivered a vocal blast such as the oxen were supposed to understand, and the big wagons were slowly but surely eased to dry ground and on toward Fort Macleod.

The average load for a Red River cart was between 800 and 1,000 pounds. The driver, generally responsible for three or more carts in a "train," walked beside his vehicles. A train boss or captain had to ride a horse in order to keep in touch with the long line of carts, perhaps 200 or 300 traveling in a single line on main trails. One cart train leaving Fort Garry with beef and tallow for St. Paul in 1856 had 500 carts, most of them drawn by oxen.

And if oxen dominated the cart trails, they practically monopolized the heavy wagon trails south of Fort Calgary. In that more distant part where ground was generally dry, the moving of freight was left almost entirely to the famous "bull trains." The editor of the *Macleod Gazette,* on May 17, 1887, noted: "The town looked something like old times on Saturday. The main street was blocked with bull teams loaded with freight and coal." Most of the oxen congregated there would belong to the I. G. Baker Co. which had thirty-six of the heavy freight wagons and 320 oxen in service at that time.

Calgary was considered the northern terminus for bull train operation but occasionally the big outfits moved onto the softer ground leading to Edmonton. The first one went over the trail in 1885, as indicated by a news item: "A bull train belonging to I. G. Baker and Co., arrived from Calgary on Wednesday with Government supplies. This is the first train of the kind that ever came to Edmonton. It comprised nine teams, six yoke of oxen in each." (*Edmonton Bulletin,* June 27, 1885.)

A "train" might have any number of wagon units, but each unit consisted in most cases of three wagons hitched together—lead wagon, swing and trail—and drawn by eight or ten pairs of oxen hitched tandem. Such a three-wagon unit could carry up to 20,000 pounds and one man was assigned to each. When a halt was called for noon or night, the wagons were placed to form a circle with an opening at one end. This became the corral into which the work cattle

The hardy ox was in use all year round. Depending on the season he would be hitched to sleigh or wagon — if the traveler was willing to settle for a slow ride.

Winter in Edmonton, circa 1910

Saskatoon, in the early 1900's

were driven by the night herder at an early morning hour and in which each driver or skinner was obliged to identify his oxen and get them yoked for the day's work. If there were ten wagon outfits in the train, there could be as many as 150 or 200 oxen to be corralled and yoked each morning and the confusion could be considerable.

A descriptive newspaper item of 1888 seemed to be intended especially for the edification of readers of a later generation: "A team is made up of three enormous wagons, each weighing from 2,000 to 2,500 pounds and holding as high as 12,000 pounds of coal. To each are attached from 18 to 20 large oxen. The train consists of say six of these teams, or 18 wagons in all and over 100 oxen. Each team has one driver with a very long and heavy whip which he uses with great skill and appropriate language. The whole are under a wagon boss, and with a cook and a night herder make up the outfit. . . . These teams travel about 12 miles a day and carried 65 tons of hay into Macleod at one time though the usual load is from 45 to 50 tons of coal. The night herder drives the oxen to pasture, watches them and returns them for the day's work, as the animals get nothing but grass." (*Lethbridge News*, March 8, 1888.)

Much has been written about the thirty-two horses and mules driven as a team by Slim Moorehouse at the Calgary Exhibition and Stampede in 1924 and the thirty-six horses handled by the same man in the next year—both extremely notable achievements on city streets, but very little has been said about the thirty-ox team hitched to a Red River cart for the conveyance of Lord and Lady Dufferin on the occasion of their official visit to Manitoba in 1877. Rarely if ever had the lowly oxen been accorded the honor of transporting a Governor General and his lady. And rarely was such a spectacular ox team seen before or since.

The Vice-Regal couple would visit Stony Mountain, north of Winnipeg, and those who planned the trip and reception were anxious to make the official appearance memorable. Oxen, still hauling most of the freight on prairie trails and doing a big share of the work on farms, were not novelties by any means but residents of the Stony Mountain district believed they had the finest oxen to be found anywhere. Anxious to prove the point of their contention, settlers offered the best of their work cattle to make up a team the Governor General would never forget.

Hitched tandem, the thirty oxen in single file, all with massive frames and mature horns, made an outfit stretching for 300 feet. William Vincent was the man in charge, and being familiar with the perversity of oxen, he took all the proper precautions. The animals were hitched between traces which extended throughout the entire length of the outfit, and a man or a boy was assigned to walk beside each individual ox. If any animal became obstreperous or balky,

National Museum of Canada Photo

Len Hillyard photo (WDM collection)

he could be released immediately by the cutting of two ropes or straps and there would be no disruption in the remaining part of the span—and no danger to the distinguished guests riding in the cart. The precautions were quite proper, but the oxen, comprising the longest string of its kind in Canadian history, behaved with the respect befitting the occasion and the master of ceremonies had no need to use his knife on ropes or straps. (*Rockwood Echoes*, a History of the Rockwood Municipality, 1960.)

The West was still without a railroad and it was intended that the Countess would be present in Winnipeg to start the first locomotive, due to arrive by riverboat about that time. But the boat was delayed and it was only when the royal visitors were leaving Manitoba on a downstream riverboat that they encountered the new locomotive and a few flatcars loaded on barges being carried upstream behind the steamboat *Selkirk*. The visitors went ashore to make an inspection and it was then that the Countess of Dufferin mounted the little locomotive and formally christened it with her own title. The famous old engine, after doing many years of pioneer service, came to rest in the small park in front of the Canadian Pacific Railway depot in Winnipeg, one of the treasures from Canadian history, just like a Red River cart or an ox yoke or a picture of the big team of oxen at Stony Mountain.

Chapter 3

The Homesteader's Ox

SUPPLYING WAGONS and animal power to pull them was Winnipeg's most flourishing business for some years as landseekers on their westward way paused to stock up with necessities. For Winnipeg businessmen, it was easy to make sales; the problem was in obtaining the animals, especially horses which had to be brought from distant parts. Most of the oxen recruited by the dealers were two-year-old and three-year-old farm steers, sons of family milk cows, rushed to the city and given a hurried and inadequate introduction to yokes or harness. A steer worth thirty dollars for beef might bring fifty dollars as an ox. But soon after starting over the trail leading to homestead land, the purchaser discovered that his recently-acquired oxen knew as little about draft work as he knew about oxen. Hitching them was not difficult but understanding them took time.

Some of the oxen sold at Winnipeg were furnished with heavy yokes which rested on the bovine necks and were held in place with U-shaped bows. Yokes had the advantage of simplicity and economy, and there was no trouble with traces and whippletrees becoming tangled in scrub and bushes. On the prairie where wood for making yokes was difficult to find, most oxen were fitted to horse harness with the horse collars turned upside down to accommodate the peculiar shape of ox shoulders.

As the newcomer to the country drove westward, he had plenty of time to reassess his decision to acquire oxen instead of horses. With horses, he would travel faster and have less reason to swear. He could be finding a feeling of friendship with his animals. With the oxen, on the other hand, he had a somewhat smaller cash investment— perhaps one hundred dollars for the pair of oxen instead of two hundred dollars or more for a team of reliable horses— and a very greatly simplified problem in obtaining feed. In being able to "live off the land," the oxen held a particularly big advantage for the man going to a homestead farm.

Like other ruminants, the ox possessed great stomach capacity; the mature animal's four-compartment stomach would hold about as much as a rain barrel and by ingesting his fill, the animal was able to get sufficient feed energy to meet all body needs, even when working. The horse, with a relatively small stomach, needed some concentrate feed and could not work without it. In other words, the horse required oats or barley grain along with fodder feeds. Freighters might carry supplies of grains but most homesteaders could not obtain the grains and could not afford the cost even if grains were available. Instead of rationing the more costly feeds, the ox driver simply turned his animals loose at night and hoped they would be full of grass and easy to find in the morning.

The ox was good at "living off the land" in summer, but it had to be recognized that he was a failure in coping with snow-covered ranges in winter. The horse could paw his way through snow to reach the dry grass below, but the ox could neither paw like a horse nor muzzle his way through snow in the manner of the buffalo. Thus, oxen wintering outside had to look for open ranges or go hungry.

There were instances, however, when frontier resourcefulness changed the natural order. A Medicine Hat settler with two horses and two oxen faced the winter of 1886-87 with neither hay nor the resources necessary to get it. Using his imagination, he tied an ox to the halter of each horse and turned the livestock loose. Where the horses went, the oxen had to go. The horses pawed away the snow to get to grass, and the oxen, constantly at their sides, shared the available fodder. It was the most severe winter experienced by settlers in the new country, but the homesteader's horses and oxen came through with nothing more serious than some loss of weight.

There was still another economic advantage on the side of the oxen and the homesteaders did not overlook it: an ox did not necessarily depreciate in value, as an aging horse would become gradually worthless. When the horse became old or suffered a broken leg, the animal had to be written off as a total loss. Not so with the ox; he never became too old to furnish boiling beef and never so badly crippled that his owner would not think of converting him to household rations. Ox beef was tough and consumers confessed

In this re-creation from the National Film Board's **The Drylanders,** a pioneer family heads for their land armed only with the homesteaders' basic equipment — a pair of oxen, a wagon which carried the family's goods, and the most important item of all — a plow.

The homesteader begins a hard day's work, depending on his oxen and plow to help him wrest a living from the land.

The familiar bow yoke, which was favored by most pioneers, permitted the animal to carry the weight of the load on the muscles of its neck. On the Prairies however, where wood was scarce, oxen were often put into horse harness, with the horse collars turned upside down to accommodate the peculiar shape of the ox's shoulders. Eventually, ox collars were made with leather.

National Film Board Photo

National Film Board Photo

T. R. Melville-Ness Photo

to "sitting down to dinner hungry and getting up tired," but even the meat from old animals was a source of dietary protein and it had the most pronounced beef flavor. Bought at fifty dollars when two or three years of age, the ox might still have fifty dollars' worth of tough red meat in his carcass seven or eight years later.

Slaughtering an aging ox for beef was not an act of gratitude by any means but it happened rather often that the oldest of the homesteader's oxen was marked to furnish winter meat for the household.

Even at slaughtering time, the old ox could be unyielding and unimpressionable. A settler of Scandinavian origin decided to butcher his remaining ox and freeze the meat for winter consumption. All the appropriate preparations were made for the killing and dressing. A block-and-tackle used for stretching barbed wire was suspended from a tripod at the stable door, and a ring to which the old bullock would be drawn for the knocking and stunning was made fast to the stable floor. All was ready and the haltered ox was snubbed securely to the metal ring. The homesteader swung to deliver the knockout blow from the back of his ax but it made only a bruising impact upon the hard bovine skull. The man swung again, and again, with no more effect. At the fourth blow, the ox was showing signs more of anger than of collapse, threatening to lift the stable floor and be off. The homesteader paused to contemplate. A better philosopher than a butcher, he announced his decision: "He's a better ox than I realized; I think I'll keep him for another year." And so, the aged ox was granted a reprieve and went back to work much as usual, teaming with an old horse and showing no ill effect from the attempt at slaughter.

It was a misfortune which plagued the ox continually, that its meat was coveted by hungry people. Indians managed to get away with an annoying number of oxen belonging to settlers and found the meat to be no better and no worse than that of old buffalo bulls. Many of the oxen furnished by a benevolent government for use on the new Indian reserves during the 1880's came to unexpected ends at the hands of underfed tribesmen. It happened at the Blackfoot reserve that Indian Agent Magnus Begg found twelve strange oxen grazing on his grass and was immediately filled with suspicion. (As recalled by Mrs. Fran Fraser and reported by John Schmidt, *Calgary Herald*, Aug. 25, 1964, p. 8.) Thinking that he might have stolen cattle on his hands, he communicated with Indian Agent Pocklington of the Blood reserve, inquiring if any of his work cattle were missing. Pocklington replied that the government oxen had disappeared and he suspected young Blackfoot of a raiding expedition. Having failed to get the horses they wanted, the raiders took oxen instead. "Please return the animals," Pocklington pleaded.

Of course Begg would send the stolen cattle back to the other reserve and immediately notified his fellow-worker that his Blackfoot boys were on their way with ten oxen, the other two having been killed and consumed by the Blackfoot after arrival. In due course, the Blood agent replied to thank Begg for his co-operation but added that only nine oxen were delivered, another having been slaughtered and eaten en route.

Oxen could not be blamed if Indians looked upon them with longing any more than a pretty girl could be held responsible when boys glanced lasciviously. But cattle could be censured for seeking protection from flies in a slough when hitched to a wagon and supposed to be working, and they could be rebuked for their delight in demonstrating how slowly they could travel without becoming completely stationary. No other means of travel could make a short journey seem so long. Pedestrians hoping for a ride knew they could save no time by climbing onto an ox-drawn cart or wagon. The traveler on foot had a reasonable chance of overtaking an ox team but he knew that no such team would ever overtake him unless he stopped and waited.

Homesteaders returning from town on winter nights were known to catch rides with passing horse-drawn sleighs, leaving the oxen to come home alone and at their own speed. Generally, the oxen arrived at their stables in calculated time, but not always. There were times when the oxen failed to arrive and were found next day, resting and feeding at a neighbor's strawpile, still hitched to the farm sleigh.

However, those slow-moving creatures possessed a hidden potential and displayed, on rare occasions, a burst of amazing speed. Neither coaxing nor prodding was enough to make them proceed faster than a slow walk when working, but the hiss of a heelfly was sufficient to change them into galloping fiends with speed to worry a Man o' War. A Saskatchewan man who drove oxen recalled his customary prodding to maintain a speed of even two miles an hour. Then, one day, a heelfly made its terrifying buzzing and the oxen raised their tails and took off down the trail. As related by their owner: "They overtook and passed the first Model T car in our district." Adding to their reputation for cussedness and unpredictability, the normally placid oxen would occasionally stage a runaway. Winnipeg papers made record of a runaway ox team which hit some guy ropes and wrecked some property, including the Customs House flag pole (*Daily Free Press*, Aug. 12, 1874), and another pair which broke the law by exceeding the speed limit on a local bridge: "W. J. Guiler, caretaker of the Louise Bridge had a granger arrested for allowing his oxen to run over the bridge instead of walking . . . he was fined $1 and costs." (*Winnipeg Sun*, Oct. 13, 1881.)

If speed records had been kept for oxen, the Medicine Hat area might have claimed a champion. That district had fast horses and skillful horsemen and it had George Nugent's trotting ox which, in 1893, was being trained for an appearance at the World's Fair. The big ox, a cross between a Highland bull and a Mexican longhorn cow, was raised on the range near Walsh and it was there that Nugent, manager of the local C.P.R. farm, saw him. Strange as it seemed, the steer's usual gait was a trot, and when he was being pursued, a cowboy on a horse had to travel at a fast gallop to overtake him.

Nugent resolved to acquire the steer and break and train it. The plan was not easy to carry out. As a range steer, the big fellow resented humans and harness and wheels. But Nugent's patience led to mastery, and after a

Thirty-five oxen break sod on the farm of J. G. Miller, Lumsden, Saskatchewan, around 1906. Two acres were broken on every round of the field; 960 acres were broken in a season.

few months, the ox was performing well and his owner was preparing to take him to Chicago.

Named "Evader," the ox was raced at Medicine Hat and on nearby tracks where he humiliated some of the highly-rated trotting horses. Apparently, World Fair officials did not offer much encouragement and the ox did not see Chicago but he became well known around Medicine Hat where local sportsmen were ever ready to subscribe a purse for a race between their favorite ox and some itinerant standardbred horse. Picturesque, with long horns, a long tail, and an unfriendly face, the ox seemed to enjoy a race, and like a good horse, he knew how to keep a bit of extra speed for the home stretch. Men who remembered him said he could trot a mile in 2:30. It was a worthy mark for either an ox or a horse, even though Nancy Hanks, at about the same time, "chopped two seconds from the world's trotting record . . . Nancy shot under the wire at 2:05¼." (*Lethbridge News*, Sept. 7, 1892.)

Ox races were not unknown. At Saskatoon's first fair in 1886, where the prizes for oxen were bigger than those for horses, H. Donavon offered a special prize of one dollar for the best trotting ox hitched to a buckboard. In the spirited contest which followed, Mr. Kusch's red and white ox won the dollar and the high honor.

At the same pioneer show, another special prize was offered for "the best walking team" and Stanley King entered his oxen against the horse teams. The horsemen protested the entry of oxen, contending that horses had exclusive claim to the term "team," and two oxen could be nothing more than a "pair" or "yoke." The executive committee of the fair was called to adjudicate and ruled that two oxen constituted a legitimate "team" and surprisingly, King's oxen won the first prize.

Homestead owners of oxen did not go in for showing at fairs but they vied quietly to own the biggest specimens in the community. Quality in a horse or an ox was always open to dispute; weight could be confirmed on the elevator scales and most arguments about size in cattle and horses were settled by the agent. It was a time when big steers, petticoats, and bustles were in fashion. The steer entry which won the championship at the Manitoba Provincial Exhibition in St. Boniface, 1886, was Big Ben, tipping the scales at 2,650 pounds. And back on the farms and homesteads were old oxen with enough size to make the St. Boniface champion appear commonplace. A few of the big individuals were brought to public display, among them the giant ox from Pibroch, Alberta.

Here was a Shorthorn, calved near Wetaskiwin and bought by C. W. Parsons of Pibroch. At five years of age, the animal weighed 3,170 pounds and was sent to the Brandon Exhibition where anybody paying a twenty-five-cent admission charge could see him. Display at Calgary and Edmonton exhibitions followed, and he was sold for $350, "a mint of money at that time," Mr. Parsons said. The ox continued to grow and was shipped to England to be exhibited at the British Empire Exhibition at Wembley in 1924 and 1925. They said he was the sensation of the cattle world, "a 4,000-pound ox, the biggest in the world." Nobody disputed the claim. At such a weight, the animal would be bigger than England's famous Durham ox which weighed 3,024 pounds at five years of age and 3,400 pounds at ten years and won a place in English history. The Alberta-bred ox looked like a proper teammate for Paul Bunyan's "Big Blue Ox," hero in hundreds of lumber-woods legends.

Many of the pioneer oxen became big; a few possessed more speed than they ever revealed; but the characteristic common to all was obstinacy. And when users spoke about "Buck and Bright" being exasperating, nearly always they could support their opinions with evidence. Carl Stone, of Crossfield, could tell of a homestead neighbor who went visiting every Sunday afternoon and always traveled in slow comfort, driving his oxen hitched to a stoneboat. This was the neighbor who allegedly never tasted water until he arrived at the homestead and had difficulty in adapting to the uninspiring beverage. On one of those Sunday visits, the trip home was delayed far into the night and when the

Some impatient newcomers couldn't wait for spring—they got an early start out of Edmonton, hurrying to reach their homesteads in the Peace River country, circa 1910.

National Museum of Canada Photo

reveler was ready to hitch for the drive, the oxen had disappeared.

All next day and all the next were spent in hunting through the hills and coulees for the wayward critters and the foot-weary settler was about ready to give up. He returned home and before turning in for the night, happened to enter his sod-covered stable. There were the lost oxen. Having broken away from the neighbor's stable, they wandered back to familiar quarters and in order to be away from mosquitoes and flies, went inside and found the solitude and comfort they could appreciate.

One of the ox-driving farmers in the Melfort community, having no well on his place, hauled water by means of barrels and stoneboat from a distant spring — two barrels at a time. He insisted that the oxen would never take a drink when they were at the water hole; they were not thirsty then. But by the time they arrived back home and much of the water had been lost by splashing from the barrels, the oxen were thirsty and would drink all or nearly all the remaining water. Then it was time to go over the trail for more water.

But oxen, the poor man's source of power, were soon to disappear from western farm scenes. Displaced by horses and mechanical power, they became novelties and memories in the West. Only in the Canadian Maritimes did they survive with any semblance of importance. A westerner attending the old fair at Windsor, Nova Scotia, in 1962, saw nothing more intriguing than the twenty-one teams of oxen in the arena show ring at one time. There, the ox user walked in front of his charges rather than behind, hitched with horn yokes rather than bow yokes, and had words of praise for his sleek oxen rather than apology.

Nobody would want to bring them back to the West, but it should not be forgotten that for more than a decade, oxen were the principal source of power for trails and farms. Exasperating as they might be, they made a fundamental contribution to progress and it is difficult to imagine how the homesteaders would have operated without them. Surely, they were the unsung heroes of the frontier. Homesteaders had words of praise and affection for their horses while their oxen rated little more than derision. Beecham Trotter, pioneer horse dealer at Brandon, was right in what he wrote about the ox: "Everybody used him, nobody praised him, though he was patient under affliction, constant in toil and frugal in his diet." (*A Horseman and the West*, Macmillan Co. of Canada, 1925, p. 237.)

The sullen bovine behavior did not invite endearment, but on performance, the ox earned more gratitude than he received.

Chapter 4

The Mysterious Mule

FOR A CREATURE hopelessly handicapped by sterility, the mule has had a surprisingly long history. For at least 2,000 years before its raucous voice was heard in the New West, this melancholy-looking hybrid was caught in controversies about suitability for farm work. The early Grecian, Homer, preferred the mule to the ox for plowing, and Cato, Roman authority on farm management, fancied the ox but admitted that an ass or a mule might be more economical to feed.

Mules were never very numerous in Western Canada. Neither were tractors with wooden wheels, but they were sources of interest and subjects for debate. Nearly every district had at least one farmer who had faith in mules. In most instances, he was an immigrant from the United States and brought mules with him, like Roy Monsees who came from Missouri to settle at Melfort, Saskatchewan, or William Russell who came from Kansas to live at Chigwell, Alberta. These men brought their mules by railroad. Occasionally, a carload of mules cleared the Canadian customs at the boundary to be delivered to some district with a preponderance of American settlers. It might be the shipment "destined to the Mormon Settlers at Lee's Creek." (*Lethbridge News*, Aug. 24, 1893.)

Immigrants who were not in a hurry drove mules and covered wagons from Kansas or Missouri, among them that unidentified and unlucky landseeker whose four mules vanished in the night while he was still on the trail leading to a homestead. Either the mules strayed or they were whisked away by marauding Indians. In any case, the immigrant was stranded hopelessly until a benevolent horseman traveling that way presented him with four broncos.

Russell brought horses and mules when he came to Alberta in 1907 but lost most of the former from swamp fever and argued that mules were more resistant to disease and frontier hardship. Of the mules he brought, one lived to be thirty-nine years of age and another forty-two years, testifying to mule longevity.

Roy Monsees, on the other hand, depended entirely upon mules and was known to say that if he could not farm with mules, he would not farm at all. He would offer many reasons for his devotion to mules. In the Deep South where mules were numerous, they were known to be far ahead of horses in resistance to both heat and disease. Monsees argued that his mules could face the cold of Saskatchewan winters with no more hardship than that felt by his neighbors' horses, and the eighteen or twenty head running in his fields during winter months seemed to prove the point. His main criticism was that his mules working in the fields "counted the rounds and refused to make more than ten." That was fair enough as long as they were working in half-mile fields because ten miles in half a day was as much as anybody expected; but when they were working in a potato patch a few rods long, the mule idiosyncrasies could create problems.

Having come from a mule-raising community in Missouri, Monsees was qualified to speak authoritatively about the hybrid offspring from a mare and a jackass. Although the average mule was smaller than its horse parent and bigger and more muscular than the donkey, it was, in the opinion of its friends, a better worker and tougher than either parent. Under saddle, the mule rarely won a race against horses, but farmers cared little about running speed as long as the animal was good at the walking gait. Dealers and farmers favored the bigger mules, those weighing 1,000 to 1,200 pounds, and breeders were advised to select the bigger mares for crossing.

In winning human affection, mules were not particularly successful and did not seem to care. Canadians were guilty of some prejudice and never gained a proper understanding of the long-eared workers. Socially, a mule farmer ranked only a few points above a man with oxen and had no hope of being accepted as an equal with the horsemen. Mules came with a reputation; they were supposed to be ornery and treacherous, and the reputation — just or unjust — stuck like a fly in a gluepot. When somebody was said to be "stubborn as a mule" or something-or-other was described as having "a kick like a mule," the inferences were neither flattering nor fair to the mule.

Was it not the alleged kicking propensity of the Iowa mule that induced the celebrated Bob Edwards of *Calgary Eye Opener* fame to leave the Central States and come to Canada? After a spell as a Wyoming cowboy, Edwards drifted eastward and became a hired man on the Clay County farm in Iowa. But the endless chores and long hours —five in the morning to eight at night—ended all thought of becoming a cornbelt farmer. The experience with the mule was the crowning touch in driving him to search for another vocation.

It was haying time and Edward's job was to drive the little mule hitched to a rake. Having finished the work in a certain field, he returned to the barnyard as darkness was settling over the countryside. After taking the harness off the mule and allowing the animal to go to the stable unattended, he followed in due course, expecting to find the animal in its own stall. But, as Bob Edwards related later, the farm milk cow, which normally occupied the next stall, had been sick and failed to eat the ration of grain placed in the manger for her. Sensing some good eating, the mule went into the cow's stall instead of its own.

"Later, in the darkness," Bob Edwards wrote, "I came with milk bucket in hand and entered the stall and started to milk the animal standing there. Three hours afterwards I recovered consciousness and my farming days were over."

At this point, Bob Edwards came to Canada.

Roy Monsees argued that the mule was no more of a kicker than the horse. Perhaps hybrid vigor put more power behind the kick from a mule, but in kicking its way out of harness and all attachments to farm implements, the bronco horses brought to western farming communities far outclassed the mules. But still the mule myth persisted.

On one point, the mule's limitations in breeding, there was no room for doubt or argument. In a few rare instances, female mules produced offspring but for all practical purposes, the mule was a non-breeder. Such was a handicap, but as Roy Monsees observed: "Your geldings don't reproduce either."

For a person choosing to raise his own mules, it was simply a matter of selecting suitable mares and acquiring a jackass. A few settlers from the United States, like Farley Morrical, of Clive, brought jacks with them and used them extensively. The arrival of a jack made more news than the importation of a stallion, and nobody was surprised to read about Christopher Fahrni having arrived back from the United States with a "full-blooded Spanish jack. The animal is a fine four-year-old, fourteen hands high and weighs 1,000 pounds." *(Daily Free Press,* Winnipeg, March 30, 1876.)

Those who claimed that mules could outpull horses of the same weight might have had trouble proving it, but there was no doubt about the mule's superiority in hardiness, durability of feet, sure-footedness, and ability to sense and stay out of danger. The horse getting a foot or leg in barbed wire would struggle and compound its own trouble while the mule would become passive and avoid aggravation of a wound. Thus there were tangible advantages, enough to result in mule prices ranging 10 to 20 per cent higher than prices for horses.

A western farmer writing in 1908 made a strong case for the relative simplicity of mule care: "When you come in at night, take the harness off the mules and turn them into the lot. They will go right out and take a roll, drink a little, take another roll, eat a bit, lie down, get up and eat a little more, take another drink, roll again and then eat some more. They know just what they want to do to make themselves feel comfortable and that's more than a horse does. In the morning your mules are ready for another hard day's work, and you haven't had to rub the stiffness out of their legs or touch a brush or comb to them. You can work them hard every working day in the year, and at the end of that time you will find that the mules have grown all the time, have taken on flesh, and that there isn't a cripple or foundered animal in the whole bunch." (*The Journal of Agriculture and Horticulture,* Montreal, June 1, 1908).

Horsemen did nothing in trying to understand mules but they had to admit the disposition was fascinating. These sultry brutes, said to have "no pride of ancestry or hope of posterity," could be stubborn but they were generally placid, even sluggish, and more philosophical than treacherous. They had their whims. Men who drove them maintained that they hated to get their feet wet. There were stories about immigrants standing at midpoints of small streams, holding pans of oats and pleading with the wary mules to cross. They had strong views about such matters as quitting time, speed of travel, and amounts of feed. Most of them had more sense about eating and drinking than horses—more, perchance, than the men who drove and cared for them—and would refuse to overeat at any time or drink too much when overheated. Roy Monsees could release his mule teams to eat grain from the open door of a granary at noon, with no fear that they would gorge themselves and become victims of colic.

And true to tradition, they could be mysterious and foxy. John Grant, who walked from Winnipeg to Brandon and began farming there in 1879, told about a mule-driving neighbor taking home a load of coal and becoming stuck on the 18th Street hill on Brandon's north side. If

Farmers who preferred mules to horses were a minority, but they were a loyal minority. In some prairie regions, the hybrids provided power for several years. Although the animals were known for their stubbornness, their owners claimed they had more sense than horses.

T. R. Melville-Ness Photo

the loaded sleigh was not stuck, at least the mules believed the load was too heavy and should be stuck. They could see no reason for straining their muscles on it. At this point, John Grant came along, driving a team of horses and an empty sleigh, and offered to hitch his drafters in front of the mules and thereby help to pull the load to the top of the hill. He unhitched and placed his team in position, tandem fashion, only then to discover that neither he nor the neighbor had a chain by which the front team could be connected with the load.

"Let's try it without the chain," said the neighbor. "You just drive in front. If my mules think they're getting help, they may take the load out all right."

John Grant did as instructed, and the mules, satisfied that the horses were sharing the burden, leaned into the collars and took the load of coal to the top of the hill without much trouble. Then the horse team was taken back to the Grant sleigh and the mules went on their way, contented with the recognition their protest and work stoppage had received.

"You have to be careful that they don't outguess you," Roy Monsees said. And then he related the experience with two mules hauling the water tank for a steam threshing outfit in the Melfort district. It was late in the season and the slough from which water was being obtained was frozen over. The tank man's practice was to back the tank onto the ice, cut a hole to water and pump until the tank was full. But on one of those trips, the heavy load of water was too much for the ice and the hind wheels broke through. The driver tried the mules to see if they could extricate the loaded tank. Having sensed the trouble, the mules were quick to conclude their inability to budge the load. The man knew the consequences if he were delayed very long; the threshing machine would be obliged to idle and that would never do. If the mules could not draw the loaded tank from the hole into which it had dropped, his only alternative would be to drain the water, get the wheels back on the ice and start to pump again. Once more he urged the mules to lift the load from the slough, and again they were unsucessful. The driver was worried and annoyed, believing that the team could take the tank out of the ice if there was the will to do it. Then, just as he was about to open the tap to lighten the load or empty the tank, the engineer at

Slim Moorehouse drove his thirty-two-horse-and-mule outfit from Buffalo Hills, east of Vulcan, to the Calgary Exhibition and Stampede in 1924. The outfit was a full city block long and was controlled with four pairs of reins (to the first, sixth, twelfth and lead teams). Turns at street corners were made with difficulty.

Oliver Studios Photo

the threshing outfit blew the steam whistle to notify all members of the crew for miles around that it was time to stop for the noon meal. The mules pricked up their long ears and thought of the folly of spending a noon hour beside a frozen slough and far from feed rations. Without waiting for the driver to collect the reins, the sagacious brown fellows settled down to pull and with a little extra effort, drew the loaded tank from the hole in the ice and were on their way to the thresher when the driver overtook them.

The big-headed, long-eared, thin-tailed, pony-footed creatures might appear melancholy and dull, but there was nothing stupid about them and as pioneer laborers, they performed well. Being "tougher than horses and faster than oxen," they caught the attention of freighters and contractors as well as American settlers. It was noted at Winnipeg that a mule team "with supplies for the Mounted Police at Pelly left today." (*Daily Free Press,* April 12, 1876.) And in reviewing railway construction, John Blue (*Alberta Past and Present,* Pioneer Historical Publishing Co., 1924, p. 342) estimated the number of mules imported in 1909 and 1910 to be 5,000. As construction work was completed, many of the mules were sold to farming people.

Missouri may have been the Mule State in the neighboring country. In Canada, the biggest mule populations were in Saskatchewan and Alberta, where the largest number of Americans settled to farm. The *Canada Year Book* showed the Dominion mule population as 15,102 in 1919, with all the animals counted being in the western provinces. But provincial figures did not agree; they showed 14,522 mules in Saskatchewan alone and almost 5,000 in Alberta. In the United States at the same time, with horse population at roughly 20,000,000, mules numbered about 5,000,000.

Mules could hold their own with horses or oxen without much trouble but in competition created by the new tractors, they were no more successful than the other draft animals and their numbers fell quickly. In Alberta where statisticians counted 4,726 mules in 1916, numbers were down to 3,772 in 1921, to 2,102 in 1931, to 922 in 1941, and 365 in 1946. By 1951, the Alberta mules had either disappeared or their numbers were so low that they were not considered to be worth counting and recording.

Chapter 5

Horses for Homesteads

THE SETTLER'S first choice was for horses, even when he bought oxen. He had to be practical and deny himself many of the good things for which he yearned. He would settle temporarily for the cattle for reasons of economy and their ability to live and work on grass and hay, but he was well aware of the shortcomings of oxen. The ornery fellows took too long on the trail, walked too slowly in the fields, and compelled the most upright Methodists to use profanity—apparently the only language to which the critters would listen.

From the very day of purchase, it was the homesteader's resolve to dispose of his oxen and buy horses when circumstances would permit. He promised himself that he would grow grain, provide proper stabling for horses, and pray for protection from glanders, swamp fever, and horse thieves. If he could not buy four horses at one time, he would buy two or one, even though he would have to hitch horses and oxen together to make up a four-animal or three-animal team for plow and binder. The records show many field teams each consisting of two horses and two oxen, also of those comprising two horses and one ox or two oxen and one horse. In any case, the new farmer would not be satisfied until horses had displaced the last of his oxen.

Angus Mackay, driving from Winnipeg to Indian Head in 1882, and W. R. Motherwell, driving from Winnipeg to a homestead on the north side of the Qu'Appelle Valley in the same year, were typical of thousands on the twisting trails leading to free farms. They were thankful to have draft power of any kind, even oxen, but both were reminding themselves that after one good crop they should be in a position to get horses. Robert Sinton, on the trail at the same time and going to Regina, had already graduated from oxen to horses and was overtaking and passing most of the ox drivers the way a man with a Cadillac might be passing fellow travelers with more humble transportation in a later generation. Sinton, four years earlier, had driven oxen from Winnipeg to a homestead near Rapid City and made enough progress to enable the change to horses before deciding to move again, this time to the place known as Pile of Bones and likely to be fixed upon for the capital of the Northwest Territories.

Oxen marked their drivers as freshman farmers; horses were symbols of progress. Oxen aroused no sentiment; horses, the oldtimers of the barnyard set, were the undisputed aristocrats. Long association with North American soil should have given the latter some degree of preferment, at least some special respect in homestead country. Alas, those "first family" connections were largely unnoticed by homesteaders, whose interest was strictly utilitarian. Horses would pull plows to convert the confirmed sod into wheat fields. That was the main consideration. They would pull discs and harrows and seed drills and binders without which there could be no farming as the newcomers envisioned it. They would take wagons loaded with grain over long roads and trails to towns and return with lumber and tools and tons of supplies. And when more speed was desired, they would carry men on their backs, with or without saddles. They would do all these and still be companions with warm noses inviting friendly caresses.

Obviously, horses held the key to homestead success but still, the background story is too rich to be ignored. North American residence embracing forty million years have given the animals an ancestral history which, if they could relate it, would be the greatest story of all.

The moving narrative, as confirmed on the fossilized pages of the rocks, began with a miniature form described as Eohippus or the Dawn Horse, about as big as a present-day fox terrier dog and not as impressive in appearance. Lacking a very satisfactory means of protection, the little horse chose to remain in hiding places furnished by shrubbery and became a swamp dweller. It and its kind fancied the feed available there, although the exact nature of the favored diet must remain in doubt. With four toes on each front foot, three on each hind foot, well-developed canine teeth and a relatively small stomach, there were hints of Eohippus departing from the strict habits of a vegetarian feeder. It may have varied its diet by digging tasty bugs

The new farmer would not be satisfied until horses had displaced the last of his oxen. If he could not buy four horses at one time he would buy two, hitching them with his oxen to make up a three-animal or four-animal team.

Western Development Museum Photo

from the mud and it may have indulged in an occasional meal of fresh or stale meat from small land animals.

The primitive horse's diet, however, is speculation. What is beyond reasonable doubt is the fossil evidence of size and general form, which must appear strange to anyone familiar with the modern specimens. With hind legs longer than the front ones, a roached back, a lot of toes, and an odd way of running, the appearance would be enough to cause a modern representative of the family to shy with fright and try to run away.

But the tiny creature possessed the courage and determination to survive and draw itself upward on the evolutionary ladder. Taking to higher ground, it needed and gained added speed but found the manifold toes to be a handicap. Nature helped to overcome that impediment, and gradually, the feet changed to meet the new environment. Central toes enlarged to become hoofs and other toes, being more and more superfluous, receded upward on the shank and practically disappeared. The new front foot would correspond to the middle finger of a human hand and the new hind foot to the middle toe of a human foot, with all other fingers and toes becoming nonfunctional and nonevident.

The move to higher and drier ground led to larger numbers, and with the passing of time, horses became bigger, faster and bolder. Type variations appeared, some strains being much bigger than others. Certain of the emerging sub-species had horses as big as anything seen today. And total population must have been very huge. Horses were a dominating race for some millions of years.

Nobody can be sure when the first man-creatures entered the North American continent—maybe 25,000 years ago, maybe longer. Coming from Asia, they probably entered at Bering Strait where the two continents connected or almost connected. They would migrate southward through the Mackenzie River valley and see horses and other wild animals in such abundance as they had never experienced before. If they had been hungry for meat, they would want to stay. They were arriving too late to see dinosaurs but they would see mastodons, mammoths, and camels, as well as horses. That the horse stock was still on the continent has been confirmed by the horse bones and stone artifacts found together at ancient campfire sites. The horse was considered good eating by primitive people in Europe, and no doubt, the early North Americans found it equally appetizing.

For reasons unknown, the horses lost their grip upon the western world and disappeared. Was it because of the changing ice-age climate? Was it a case of disease or famine or predators? Was it the pressure of humans and their upsetting effect upon a delicate natural balance? Nobody knows the answer, but whatever the force, it proved deadly and resulted in complete extermination of horses in the Americas, which may have been the real birthplace of the race.

Fortunately, horses as well as primitive men could cross at Bering Strait at certain periods, and no doubt, members of the horse family moved into Asia, multiplied, fanned out across the steppes and felt at home. Thus, by the time the curtain of extinction was being drawn over the race in the Americas, horses were flourishing in the Old World.

The earliest domestication took place in China and in due course, domesticated horses were taken to the Mediterranean countries, Arabia, North Africa, and Spain. The latter country holds special importance in the story because Spaniards, following Columbus to the New World, brought horses and reintroduced them to the native land. Hernando Cortez, landing on the North American mainland in 1519, had sixteen Spanish horses with him. For members of the horse family, whose ancestors once occupied the North American continent, it marked the completion of a circle; members of the race had traveled around the world and were now back on the soil of their forebears.

The continent had been horseless for so long that the Spanish horses, landed on the coast of the Gulf of Mexico, were completely strange—even fearsome—to the Indians who saw them. But it did not take the natives long to recognize the benefits they could derive by having horses and they set out to get them by any means possible. Some Spanish horses were abandoned and recovered by the Indians. Some were stolen. Some escaped from Spanish owners, and after adopting the wild state, gave rise to the mustang strain which became a perpetuating source of horse stock for the tribesmen.

First of the Indians to see the Spanish horses and first to obtain and ride the new stock were the Comanches, but men of other tribes were quick to follow the example. Like a new weapon of warfare, it was essential that adversary tribes have them, and the way to get them was by stealing. Horse stealing became the greatest of all Indian occupations, both a game and a gainful pursuit. Thus, horses were stolen from one tribe to the next until all the western Indians had them. The first of the animals tracing to Spanish stock appeared in the Bow River valley in what is now Alberta about 1730. They were being ridden by Snake invaders from the south and braves of the Blackfoot tribes knew they had to have them. The Blackfoot stole horses from their southern neighbors; the Cree stole from the Blackfoot and the Assiniboine stole from the Cree.

Consequently, when the Selkirk settlers came to Rupert's Land and the homestead crowd was making its way into the Canadian West, the Indians had horses. They might appear thin and poorly kept but they were well climatized, hardy, sure-footed and big enough for most frontier tasks. The chief difficulty: there were not enough of them to accommodate all needs.

As Angus Mackay, who was to play an important part in the introduction of Marquis wheat, and W. R. Motherwell, who was to become a foremost figure in Canadian agriculture, plodded toward "the promised land," urging their oxen as they traveled, a few imaginative writers were speculating cheerfully about the chance of engines driven by steam or gasoline moving into farm fields and providing power to pull plows. To most people, the idea was fantastic. Newcomers to the land were not looking that far into the future. Their hope, a practical one, was to have horses—soon—and forget about anything as remote and fanciful as tractors. But one nagging question remained: where could people get horses in numbers likely to be needed?

Indians with the semi-native strains could supply only a small fraction of the animals sure to be wanted, and the horse population could not be changed quickly, like rabbits or mice or even farm pigs. It would take four years from the time a mare was bred until her offspring would be ready for the painful experience of wearing harness. There was no way of accelerating the processes of reproduction.

Immigrants had been told that they could buy horses in the areas to which they were going, but the assurance was misleading. With thousands of landseekers entering the West, available horses fell far short of demand. Some settlers, of course, brought horses with them from the East or the United States. Alternatively, it was possible to obtain horses in limited numbers from local sources, including the Indian reserves. Farmers already established in the country could be expected to have surplus animals; dealers who could get imported stock would be glad to make sales, and ranchers had horses of the bronco order.

A purchaser could be defrauded whichever way he turned to buy. Farmers in the country were not likely to part with any except their unsound or decrepit animals, and dealers bringing horses from Ontario or Wisconsin were notorious for their conscienceless gathering of equine misfits barely able to have their advanced years, broken wind, and stringhalt concealed. The only characteristic making them attractive to the dealer as he searched eastern communities was the low price, and he knew that if they were able to cling to life until they reached Manitoba, he could sell them at a good profit.

The only apparent benefit the West held for those aging eastern horses was in making them "younger."

Horses were a symbol of progress—they could do all the heavy work that oxen could and in addition they could carry men on their backs. In this old photo, a farmer clears new land at Portage la Prairie.

In almost all the work performed by a farmer of the period his horses were his helpers and partners. When he plowed, harrowed, disced, drilled, and harvested his horses furnished the power. As his wealth increased, so did the number of horses. Breaking prairie, early 1900's

Although ages, as known to their eastern owners, ranged from twelve to twenty years, the animals were generally "eight-year-olds" and "nine-year-olds" when offered in the West. An Ontario farmer who moved to the West recognized an eastern horse being offered for sale as a nine-year-old. "He's carrying his age very well," he said, very much to the dealer's embarrassment. "He was seventeen when I sold him down there and that's three years ago. At that time, he was blind in one eye. Yes, by golly, he's still blind in that eye."

The bronco breed was tough and difficult, totally hostile towards stables, harness, humans, and farm implements. Horses from the ranges came to the homestead districts with all their bad manners showing clearly. They might be "halter broken," but that was all, and it was up to the purchaser to try to make workhorses of them. Men with ranching experience knew how to break the wild ones, but the bronco rebelliousness frightened the newcomers from the East, making them wish they had remained with oxen—or remained in Ontario. Where two or more broncos were hitched together, they were sure candidates for a runaway with the usual aftermath of wreckage. But for the man with patience and judgment in handling horses, the broncos could settle down to become useful and moderately reliable workers.

Generally, the ownership of horses loomed as a bright and happy prospect in those areas where nearly everything people wanted to do required power beyond what they could accomplish with their own hands. But there was another side to ownership: regardless of where they were obtained, those precious animals could bring heartaches as well as satisfactions for their frontier owners. As farming people discovered, sometimes to their sorrow, horses lacked the foolproof qualities of oxen and seemed to have a penchant for getting into trouble. They were subject to more diseases and parasites; they could walk blindly into serious trouble with barbed wire and be incapacitated for weeks and months. They required regular feeding and clean feed. Dusty hay or spoiled grain made them sick. The horse's stomach was easily upset and every horseman knew what it was to sit up all night with a horse suffering from colic.

Some animals took colic regularly, as if they enjoyed the medicine or found they could use illness as a means of escaping from work now and then. A shot of whisky was supposed to bring relief in cases of colic, but homesteaders were loath to spend such lovely medicine on a horse if something more commonplace would serve as well. Hence the more usual treatment was a concoction made from two teaspoons of baking soda and one teaspoon of ginger in a pint of cold milk and administered as a drench from a heavy whisky bottle kept for the purpose.

Western Development Museum Photo

Bureau of Publications, Regina, photo

There was no proof that the medication did the least bit of good except to sooth the feelings of the horseman and make him think he was doing something for his sick animal.

The worst of the frontier disorders affecting horses was swamp fever. In later years it qualified for a more fancy name, infectious anemia, but nothing changed the settlers' dread of it. It was particularly prevalent in areas where horses were feeding on either grass or hay from low-lying and swampy meadows. The exact cause was not understood in those years and no effective remedy was found but horsemen were familiar with the symptoms—too familiar. Horses became thin and had intermittent fever, loss of strength, and a staggering gait as if intoxicated. In most cases, there was an early death and a period of genuine mourning while the homesteader wondered how he could operate with the unexpected shortage of horsepower.

What was a man to do when he lost horses and did not have enough remaining to pull a seed drill or binder? He might be successful in purchasing replacements with promissory notes. More likely, he would pool power resources with a neighbor to make up one complete outfit, which would be required to do the work on two homestead farms, and hope he would be able to save enough money in the remainder of the year to buy horse replacements, all the while praying that swamp fever would not strike again.

Chapter 6

When Every Farmer Was a Horseman

AS WESTERN CANADA became a land of farmers, it became a stronghold for heavy horses. Every farmer was a horseman—generally an expert—and every farm boy aspired to be an expert horseman. Saskatchewan and Alberta, in 1906, had 176,000 horses, enough to allow each of the 22,900 farm operators to hitch a four-horse or six-horse team and have one additional horse for driving and a spare in the stable in case of a colic casualty.

Often that spare was a mare with a foal but motherhood brought no guarantee of exemption from field work. Brood mares worked right up to the time of foaling and then intermittently as need arose. The double burden of nursing and field work was too much, and the mare lost weight rapidly. But what was the alternative? The brutal fact was that life for farm horses of that period was never easy; too often it was cruel. It was a case of too much work, too few draft animals, or too little feed.

Loss of weight in his animals was enough to sadden any horseman, and he tried to avoid it or minimize it. Failing all else, he tried to hide it. Every horseman was sensitive about the image created by his animals. His own reputation was at stake, and he wanted them to look their best. If they were thin at seeding time or at harvest, there could be a plausible excuse, but there was no excuse for a man's horses appearing with overgrown hoofs, unattended harness sores, or ungroomed coats. Every stable had brushes, currycombs, and the means of trimming hoofs and relieving harness sores. They were supposed to be used.

No worker pleaded ignorance. Everybody was supposed to have some understanding of horses, and pleading ignorance would have been more humiliating than admitting inability to read and write. Hired men were selected for competence in handling horses. They might be expected to milk cows and feed pigs as added chores, but the all-important part of their work was with teams and their qualifications were assessed accordingly. "Martingales," "sweatpads," "hamestraps," and "snorting poles" were parts of the everyday vocabulary. Such terms might not appear in the public-school readers but they were heard at country spelling matches and they were sure to enter into farm conversation, both in the stable and in the kitchen. Until a boy could speak the special language of horsemen and determine a horse's age by an examination of the teeth, he was not ready to face the world.

Every farm boy with ambition dreamed of the joy of driving to town on a Saturday afternoon with a team of prancing drafters, decked out with top collars, polished harness, and celluloid spread-rings to command the attention and admiration of the girls as well as men on the streets. He started early to prepare for the great day. If barnyard resources would allow, he rode or drove a horse to school and gained confidence. He was still a small child when, sitting beside his father on a wagon seat or load of hay, he took the leather reins in his little hands and felt the thrill of responsibility. Nor was he much older when he grasped the four reins to a plow-team driven tandem and advanced his skills.

It was not surprising that horses occupied men's thoughts so completely. In almost all the work performed by a farmer of the period, his horses were his helpers and partners. When he plowed, harrowed, disced, drilled, and harvested, his horses furnished the power. When he went to town for supplies, the trip was with horses hitched to buggy or wagon, and he knew his team would be scrutinized by critical horsemen along the way. When he went to a picnic, the entertainment was likely to take the form of a horse race or a game of horseshoes. When he visited neighbors, conversation would be about horses, and when he went to the weekly prayer meeting with horse hairs on his clothes, he felt no embarrassment because every other person present would be similarly marked.

It was a community made distinctive by horses and

Spring and autumn at the Miller farm in 1906 at Aylesbury, Saskatchewan. It was a large farm by prairie standards, on which eight 4-horse teams were used at the same time to provide power at seeding and harvesting.

Mrs. Charles Hay Photos

When the horseman went to town, he knew his team would be scrutinized by critical horsemen along the way, so he spent some extra time sprucing up his horses, especially if he was taking his girl for a drive in a surrey with the fringe on the top.

Western Producer Photo

because those animals required constant supervision and care, even when idle, it was impossible to get away from them. In spring and autumn when field work was pressing, the horseman's day began around four thirty. It was an hour when enthusiasms were depressed and young fellows ejected from their beds had misgivings about careers in farming. But the morning chores of watering, feeding, grooming, harnessing, and cleaning of stables had to be performed before the human workers came to their breakfast.

The horseman stumbling through the early morning to the stable heard his charges greet him with eager calls for feed and water. The thoughtful owner believed his horses should be watered both before and after every meal and began the long day by leading the animals—two at a time—to the water trough or carrying water in pails to the horses. Hungry horses whinnied incessantly, as if their noise would hasten the feeding operation. Hay was placed in mangers as soon as watering was completed, but some of the horses were not satisfied; like boys wanting to eat their pie before consuming their meat and potatoes, they would continue pawing at their mangers, pleading for morning rations of oats or other grain. But they were supposed to be patient and munch on hay while the horseman cleaned the stable and did the harnessing. Only when he had performed all other morning chores and was ready to go for his own breakfast did his horses receive their oats from the universally-used one-gallon measure.

It did not follow that the concentrate ration would consist of an even gallon of grain. Horsemen tried to vary grain allowances according to the amount of work the animals were doing. An old rule called for one pound of grain per day for every hundred pounds of live weight for horses at heavy work. Accordingly, a 1,600-pound horse performing field work would rate sixteen pounds of grain feed per day, with about one-quarter of the day's total given in the morning, one-half at noon when feeding time had to be limited, and finally, one-quarter at night when the animal would have ample time to meet the immediate body demands by eating fodder.

Farmers planned to be in the fields or, at least, on their way to the fields by seven o'clock. It was better to get a big share of the work done before the excessive heat of midday, and moreover, with the usual brief rest periods, it would take almost five hours to travel the desired eight or ten miles—eight or ten rounds on the half-mile stretch—before noon.

In the field as in the stable, the good horseman maintained constant vigilance and was able to prevent troubles leading to suffering on the part of the horses and to loss of time. Regularly, when stopped at the end of a field, he would lift the horses' collars to cool the skin and allow inspection of the shoulders. Sore shoulders were likely to be serious handicaps to working animals, but as the observant horsemen knew, they could be prevented. The first precaution was in the choice of collars. As with men's boots, collars should be of proper size and shape. And after being fitted to a collar and wearing it until it had molded itself to the exact character of the shoulders, the horse should have had exclusive claim to it, just as the horseman had exclusive claim to the boots he had worn until they had taken the shape of his feet. If and when irritation or inflammation occurred at some point on the shoulder, an intelligent adjustment by means of a sweatpad was enough to overcome the trouble. Similarly, a pad placed where needed was enough to prevent a harness sore and prevent needless suffering and inefficiency in working.

Injury, of course, came to both horses and horsemen in many forms. Handling horses was never a particularly safe occupation. If farming accounted for more accidents than either construction or mining, it was because of the unpredictable ways of horses. "Head-on" collisions did not occur, and there was no such thing as rolling an outfit over at sixty miles per hour, but there were hazards of many other kinds. A horse could kick its driver or handler with sledgehammer force and break bones or it might step on a human foot and use its 1,600 or 1,700 pounds of weight to inflict crushing damage and leave the horseman limping for weeks.

But the most feared of all accidents were those resulting from a runaway. It could occur on the road or in the field and horses as well as horsemen were candidates for serious injury. Some horses, especially those of the bronco breed which feared all humans and hated domestication, were ready to bolt at the least provocation. The sudden appearance of a jackrabbit, a piece of paper caught up in the wind, or the awful sight or sound of an approaching automobile was sufficient to fill the nervous or partially-broken horse with wild ideas of escape.

Hauling grain to Craik, Saskatchewan, about 1910. Oat sheaves have been loaded on top of the grain to feed the horses.

Mrs. Charles Hay Photo

Jack Morton, the rough-and-ready rancher at Rosebud, might enjoy the excitement of a runaway, but most people cringed at the thought and tried constantly to prevent it. However, very few horsemen escaped the awful experience of seeing valuable horses hitched to valuable equipment dashing madly across field or barnyard, perhaps to their destruction. A runaway team at Saskatoon tore out a full half mile of barbed wire fencing and was stopped ultimately by the great weight of wire and posts being dragged. A Jack Morton team ran away with a democrat and wrecked it so completely that no part of the vehicle was worth recovering.

Occasionally, a driver's life was in special danger. A North Brandon pioneer recalled the day his hired man halted at the end of a field to allow the four horses hitched to a harrow outfit to cool off and almost lost his life in the runaway scene which followed. While the horses were standing, the man walked forward to inspect collars and harness. That was all right, but when the farm dog came suddenly into view, one of the horses took fright and plunged forward. The sudden movement frightened all the horses and with nothing more than the weight of the harrows to restrain them, they began to run. The man reached to seize the bridle of one of the horses but he was not fast enough. Nor could he get out of the way of the advancing harrow, and as the long drawbar struck him, he fell to the ground where the metal harrows with six-inch teeth caught and dragged him. He tried to roll with the advancing harrows but he could not escape the cutting and crushing force. Nobody knew how far he was dragged, but ultimately, he rolled clear of the harrows to lie bleeding and unconscious until the farm owner and his wife came by wagon to find him.

The horses continued their wild run until the harness was broken and the harrows were left behind. Amazingly, no horse was injured but the man was in serious condition. Happily for him, the farmer's wife, a former nurse, knew how to cope with such an emergency, and after a temporary dressing to the abdominal wound, the unfortunate fellow was lifted to the wagon and made as comfortable as possible for a nine-mile drive to the city hospital. And displaying the fiber of horsemen, he recovered and returned to drive the same four-horse team.

One of the most involved of frontier runaway debacles was on the famous Bell Farm at Indian Head, where Major William R. Bell was conducting an early experiment in large-scale farming. Breaking began on the big block of prairie land—almost one hundred square miles—in 1882. Some of the furrows were so long that teamsters were able to make only one round each per day. Six thousand acres were ready for crop in 1884 and it proved to be a memorable year in many respects. The harvest included 130,000 bushels of wheat, and visitors saw forty-five self-binders of the newest kind working in one field. Twenty-two workhorses were stolen from the Bell stables during a night, and there was the terrible springtime runaway with forty horses involved. Ten 4-horse teams were seeding wheat in one field when the animals hitched to a rear drill took fright at a dust-laden whirlwind and bolted. The fright was quickly and effectively communicated from one horse to another, and before the drivers had time to brace themselves, the horses in all ten outfits were running, fighting to be free from the seed drills with screaming discs. Becoming more terrified as they ran, the horses encircled the field, completely out of control. Outfits collided; wooden tongues fractured; whippletrees and singletrees snapped; harness came apart, and some of the drills lost their wheels. The drivers became helpless spectators until the horses were forced by injury or exhaustion to stop running. Some of the horses were injured so seriously that it was thought best to shoot them. Altogether, it was a day of tragedy on the big Bell Farm.

Being a horseman was not easy and it was not without danger but it was challenging, and it could be argued that the New West produced some of the best and most resourceful horsemen in the world.

Chapter 7

"Repent, Ye Traders of Horses"

CHURCH MINISTERS did not forget to warn horse dealers that they could burn in Hades for their sharp practices. "Repent of those your evil ways," the preachers intoned in solemn terms. Some of the churchmen were speaking from the bitter experience of having bargained for sound animals suitable for making pastoral calls and being left in possession of equine misfits. But the admonitions clothed in terrifying terms made no apparent difference to the ways of men in the business. What became known as a horseman's conscience was one with a wide range of flexibility. The optimistic dealers supposed they would be forgiven for offering a broken-winded horse as a "roaring good beast," a blind one as a "damned good nag that just doesn't look very good," and a bronco outlaw as one "with more pep than anything you'll ever have in your stable."

Beecham Trotter told of the young man who, after turning his back upon the church ministry as a vocation, decided to become a dealer in purebred horses. *(A Horseman and The West.)* When the decision was reported to his aging father, the old man meditated seriously for a moment and then remarked, philosophically: "Well Son, I'm disappointed but if you have decided to sell stallions, I dare say you'll bring more men to repentance than you'd ever do by preaching from a pulpit."

But horse distribution in that homestead period had to be big business and middlemen were indispensable. For decades, every westbound freight train carried cars of Ontario workhorses or cars of imported stallions billed to points like Brandon or Regina where the animals would be stabled and sold by men who classified as dealers. Being good salesmen, they radiated confidence. And, anyway, what could possibly change the horse's supremacy in the West's expanding agriculture? Instead of needing fewer horses, the farming area would need more and more of all kinds, work stock for more and bigger wheat fields, mares and stallions for the production of replacements, and light kinds to handle buggies and saddles. Farmers demonstrated their eagerness by the large number of mares they chose to breed. Isaac Beattie of the well-known Brandon firm, Colquhoun and Beattie, recalled the season when five heavy stallions, standing at the Baubier Stable on Eighth Street, were bred to a total of 607 mares without leaving the premises. Every horseman was an optimist; people could be expected to fly through the air, bird fashion, or explore on the floor of the ocean like schools of halibut before they would abandon horses for farm work.

With so much trafficking in horses, it was not surprising that dealers were accepted like grocery merchants, although they did not enjoy the same reputation for reliability. Nor could horse dealers be identified so clearly as grocers, because of the thousands of amateurs who traded only occasionally but longed for more deals.

It was quite possible for an exchange of horses — even between amateurs at trading — to bring benefit to both parties involved. More often, however, one trader gained substantially while the other found himself defrauded and left with a horse possessing all the disorders or unsoundnesses or bad habits known to the editor of the *Nor'-West Farmer.*

Most users of horses, even though they traded at times, felt unprepared for dealing with the well-practiced professionals who aimed to average at least one transaction every day. Brandon horsemen like John E. Smith and J. D. McGregor admitted that they hated to end a day without the completion of some deal. When those two worthies met on the First Street Bridge late on a summer evening, Smith inquired if his friend had enjoyed any good trading that day. It was little more than a courtesy, like asking about health in the family, but McGregor was obliged to reply that it had been a barren day. Sensing how circumstances might work to his advantage, Smith glanced at the horse McGregor was riding and remarked: "He's not much to look at but I might be able to use one like him. What do you want for him?"

"Sixty-five dollars," McGregor replied.

Smith made a more thorough inspection, knowing that

This 50-time grand champion (right) is a good example of the Percheron breed, which was orginally brought to the Prairies from France and the United States. Starlight Koncarness, champion in the fifties, was owned by Hardy Salter of Calgary.

A fine example of its breed, this Belgian sire, Paragon King, (far right, top) won a number of championships and grand championships for its owner, Dr. H. E. Alexander, of Saskatoon.

A champion Clydesdale, The President, (far right, bottom), weighed 1,950 pounds when he was junior champion at the Royal Winter Fair in Toronto in 1938. The Clydesdales were originally imported from Scotland, and Scottish settlers were irascible in their loyalty to this breed.

Strohmeyer and Carpenter Photos

sundown on a "barren day" had to work in his favor, then said: "I'll give you seventeen fifty."

Like a hungry man seeing a crust of rye bread, McGregor was interested and with only a few seconds of hesitation, replied: "It's a hell of a come down but when a man's failed to handle a dollar all day, he hates to pass up a deal. You've bought yourself a horse."

For most people living on farms, horse trading was a pastime more than a vocation, but every community had one or more horsemen for whom trading became almost an addiction. They were objects of special interest as neighbors scrutinized the rising and falling fortunes. For some men it was not a successful year unless they ended it with better horses than those with which they started. If successful, the farm trader was likely to specialize, possibly emerging as a dealer in purebred stallions.

One of the many poverty-stricken settlers near Saskatoon started out with four old horses, the only kind he could afford to buy. Their aggregate age was believed to be seventy-eight years. At best they did not have much longer for this world of endless plowing and sore shoulders, but their owner, with unrecognized talent for the game, decided to try trading as a means of improving his position. He exchanged a twenty-one-year-old gelding for a mare with a slight advantage in age and went looking for another deal of a similar kind. In the next trade, he gave an old reliable gelding with a pronounced tendency to Monday morning disease — swollen legs after a Sunday of idleness — and acquired a young horse whose chief shortcoming was nervousness due to inexperience and poor handling. Every weekend throughout the summer produced a trade, generally favorable to the homesteader, and by the time the autumn work was being completed, he was plowing with a matched outfit of bay horses, all young, all sound, altogether one of the most presentable in the community.

Good young horses did not change hands very often, but horses with broken wind or stringhalt or secret vices were constantly moving about the countryside, sampling hay and oats in widely-scattered stables. When an unsound animal became so well known that he had no more trading potential in a district, the only hope was to start him in a new area where reputation would no longer be a handicap in trading.

For those horsemen who aspired to become trading specialists, there were many opportunities. If they could escape collapse from a crippling weight of lien notes, of which every dealer had some knowledge, they had every reason to think they would do well. It was quite natural for the farmer whose local dealing was profitable to expand his activities. If he possessed the proper skill and conscience to sell horses successfully, he could not overlook the opportunity of buying cheap horses in Ontario or on the western ranges where there was a surplus, and shipping to sell at prairie points where almost anything in a horsehide and still able to walk would attract buyer interest. Ontario had an abundance of horses which, because of infirmities or advanced age, could be bought at low prices, and many dealers spent half of their time gathering up what Ontario farmers were eager to sell and the balance of their time selling from livery stables in frontier towns and villages.

The westerner hoping to purchase a carload of horses in one of those Ontario districts would announce his intention through a local eastern newspaper or by means of handbills. He would report his intention to be present at a named place on named days, and farmers were invited to bring their surplus or faltering horses for appraisal and offer to purchase. As noted by Beecham Trotter, who handled thousands of head: "When it was noticed that horses for Manitoba were required, the blind, the halt, the superannuated—everything was likely to be brought except animals in the flower of their age, well suited to withstand the change to a more rigorous climate." *(A Horseman and The West*, p. 244.)

The elite of the horse dealers were those who specialized in pedigreed stock, mainly stallions. In most cases they were men who started modestly by trading in work stock and then graduated to stallions, and the enjoyment of new prestige, and perchance, new prosperity. They maintained the most stylish homes and stables, advertised extensively, exhibited at fairs and exhibitions, drove fancy carriages and

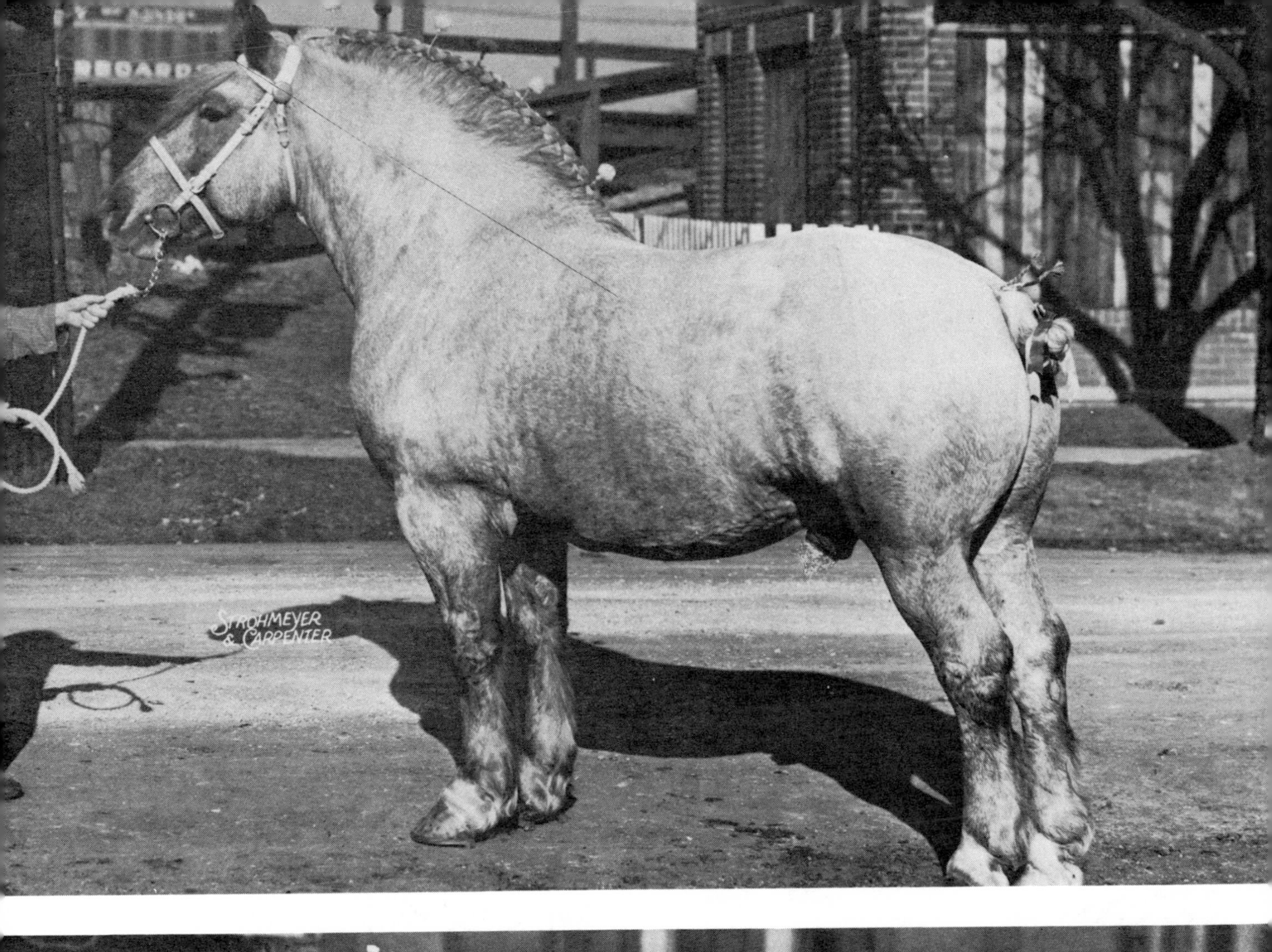
STROHMEYER
& CARPENTER

STROHMEYER
& CARPENTER

Dean of the Dealers, Alex Galbraith.

had much to say about the immutability of the horse's role in agriculture.

Winnipeg, "gateway to the New West," was the place where most settlers chose to stock up with oxen, workhorses, wagons, and other equipment of immediate importance for the trail journey and homestead. But it was not until the newcomers were well settled on the land that they considered buying stallions. Consequently, dealers found that they would be closer to the stallion and purebred mare market at Brandon or Regina or Saskatoon or North Battleford. The biggest concentration of stallion dealers was at Brandon where many horsemen with internationally familiar names conducted sales from one or another of the many livery stables. With twenty-three livery stables and about as many horse dealers in 1886, that Manitoba city was as much the Horse Capital of Canada as it was the Wheat City.

Trotter and Trotter located there in 1883 — just two years after the arrival of the railroad — and in the next few decades, according to Beecham Trotter's estimates, the company paid three million dollars for horses, mainly stallions, and shipped them to Brandon for sale and distribution. Such a sum of money would seem to represent at least 25,000 workhorses or 5,000 purebred stallions at prices prevailing at the period. Hairy-legged Clydesdale stallions with superb action were imported from Scotland, black-coated and gray-coated Percherons with symmetrical bodies were brought from France and the United States, and heavy-weight Belgians with bulging muscles were shipped from Belgium and Iowa. Isaac Beattie could tell of his firm, Colquhoun and Beattie, bringing an entire trainload of stallions to the Baubier Stable at one time and seeing all the animals being shipped out to prairie purchasers in the course of a few weeks.

If any one man deserved the title, Dean of Dealers, he was Alex Galbraith, of Brandon and Edmonton. Born in Scotland — not far from Loch Lomond — his first love, quite naturally, was the Scottish Clydesdale. But Galbraith was not guilty of pronounced breed prejudices, and horsemen of all breed preferences recognized his good judgment and reliability.

After crossing the Atlantic, Alex Galbraith settled at Janesville, Wisconsin, where, with his brothers, he imported and sold stallions — thousands of them. The business was profitable until financial panic struck in 1893. When the crash came, the Galbraith men had two boatloads of stallions on the Atlantic and the brothers faced financial ruin. The partnership was dissolved and the young men went separate ways. In 1901, however, Alex Galbraith opened a sales stable in Brandon and again his business flourished. Twelve years later, Alex Galbraith and Son opened a sales stable in Edmonton and the great horseman became an influential force in Alberta agriculture. Government officers recognized his skills and appointed him, in 1915, to the position of superintendent of fairs for the province.

Prospective purchasers of stallions turned almost instinctively to Alex Galbraith and he had patience and advice for everybody. Edmonton residents told of an out-of-city gentleman dropping in at the Galbraith stable, solely to escape from a sudden shower of rain. But the Galbraith horses seemed to captivate people, just as the Galbraith personality filled them with confidence, and by the time the shower ended, the visitor had purchased a purebred Percheron stallion and two mares.

The horse dealers as salesmen flourished across the West until light tractors became fashionable and displaced horses by the thousands. But even then the horse dealers did not disappear. For many years following, the conventional horse dealer was a man buying in the West for shipment to the East. It was a strange reversal of form. Rather suddenly, western breeders and owners were furnishing horses for a big return movement to eastern Canada, a sort of repayment for the thousands of head furnished in the formative years of prairie agriculture. Instead of sending aged animals with bog spavins and thoroughpins, however, they sent sound young horses, for which there was no further need on the mechanized farms.

Chapter 8

The Battle of the Breeds

IN BUILDING the agricultural empire of the West, no topic was debated more bitterly than that of breeds in draft horses. Sooner or later every farmer held loyalty to one particular breed and held to it tenaciously. Neither the cleavage produced by political parties nor church denominations rivaled it. Methodists and Presbyterians might seek the company of their respective kind, and Conservatives and Liberals could be expected to segregate at times, but it was on the merits of Clydesdales, Shires, Percherons, and Belgians that rural communities divided most fiercely. Nobody was neutral; either a man favored the flat-boned, hard-hocked, big-footed Clydes with straight and bold action, or he declared for Percherons or Belgians with their huge middles, powerful muscles, and phlegmatic dispositions.

Breed merits could be debated without emotion at public school, but when the question arose at the livery stable or during moments of neighborly conversation following the weekly Prayer Meeting or Christian Endeavor, tempers could flare like kerosene fires. Nothing, it seemed, could bridge the opinion gap between those who held to Clydesdales and those who favored one of the other breeds. Scottish settlers were irascible in their loyalty to the Clydesdale; people from England favored Shires but less furiously, and most settlers from the United States and mainland countries of Europe wanted Percherons or Belgians. The province of Ontario, having drawn its people very largely from the British Isles, was essentially Clydesdale country, and because many of the early settlers in the West were from Ontario, the Clydesdale held the advantage of an initial acceptance.

Until the beginning of the twentieth century, the massive, hairy-legged English Shires were the Clydesdales' only competition on the Canadian scene. At the Toronto Industrial Exhibition in 1900, with 875 horse entries, Clydesdales dominated overwhelmingly in the draft section and would have monopolized it had it not been for a few Shires exhibited. Percherons and Suffolks were known in some parts of rural Ontario and Quebec but were not sufficiently numerous to rate separate classes. Belgians were known only by pictures carried in farm magazines.

There was no doubt about the early West being Clydesdale country, just as in the East. Horsemen visiting the Winnipeg Industrial Exhibition held in July, 1900, saw hundreds of Clydesdales in the competitions, a total of two Shires and one Percheron. The Scottish horsemen could view the exhibits with smug composure, but the lone Percheron was a much bigger threat than anybody sensed. Two years earlier, George Lane, of the Bar U Ranch in the Canadian Foothills, bought the entire stud of purebred Percherons belonging to James Mauldin, Dillon, Montana—thirty-five mares in all—and drove them north to range west of High River. The importation was creating interest and giving the French breed a needed stimulus. But for most people attending the Winnipeg Industrial of 1900, the two-year-old Percheron being displayed without benefit of prize-list recognition, was the first representative of the breed they had ever seen. The *Farmer's Advocate* noted that the "black, blocky fellow of smooth pattern" was admitted for display in the judging ring and even in the absence of competition, was allowed, charitably, to take a first-prize ribbon which had gone unclaimed in the section for Shires.

At Brandon's exhibition, a few days later, breed representation was about the same: many Clydesdales, only four Shires, and no entries of any other draft breed. Until this time, therefore, most breed arguments were between the numerous supporters of Clydes and the outnumbered horsemen who favored Shires. Often it was a quarrel between Scots and Englishmen, where the fires of disagreement were never difficult to kindle. Generally, the Scots had the last word. Shire supporters inviting argument could expect a broadly-accented barrage. One of those foolhardy fellows, using the penname "Claughbane," wrote to the *Farmer's Advocate* (May 20, 1895, p. 205), saying tauntingly that the Clydesdale's popularity had to be explained by the large Scottish element existing in the country, "for there is no doubt about it, Scotchmen like things which are Scotch, and not the least among these they like Scotch horses . . . [But] the Shire is the largest breed of horses that we have and for that reason, if we would export draft horses to England, he is the sire we must use in producing them . . . We should not breed for feet and legs but for the market."

"Claughbane," it appeared, could find good in all draft breeds except the Clydesdale and in a later issue of the *Farmers' Advocate* (June 20, 1895, p. 242), he insulted the Scot's beloved Clydesdales by ignoring them and praising Percherons and Suffolks. Of Percherons, he said: "There is a very strong prejudice against them — for what reason is hard to say. . . . They are always ready to work and easily kept in condition. Another point in their favor is that they are clean-legged. And here let me say something about feather. Of what use is it? Certainly none whatever to a farm horse. It is rather a defect for it gives extra work in keeping clean and it is also an indication of poor bone. . . . The Suffolk Punch is a horse of great substance and it is surprising that there are so few of them in Canada. Why these two clean-legged breeds [Percherons and Suffolk Punch] are not in greater demand, I am at loss to understand for they are undoubtedly most suitable for getting agricultural horses."

As "Claughbane" might have expected, his irreverent treatment of the Scotsman's horse drew fire in abundance. One of the responses came from a correspondent signing as "Scotland Forever," showing unmistakable anger at anybody who would challenge his favorite breed. *(Farmer's Advocate,* July 15, 1896, p. 1288.) "Claughbane had the hardihood," wrote "Scotland Forever," "to compare the Shire with the Clyde. . . . Now, I call this nothing else but cheek. The idea of comparing a big, coarse, clumsy brute, with round bone, coarse feather and no action, with a horse that while large, has splendid action, is noted for flat, hard bone, and good feet. The Clyde is an ideal farm horse; can handle the plow and harrow in good shape and with ease to himself. . . . The Shire, on the other hand, is too slow and clumsy to be of any use on a farm. It is true, he can plow, but so can an ox, and for anything else he has not speed enough; in fact, I would advise farmers to use oxen instead, as they are just as able to get through the work, costing less, and they can be converted into beef — which the Shire cannot — a decided advantage in favor of the ox. . . . For one who finds fault with the Clyde, when compared with other draft breeds, does not know a good horse when he sees it."

The vitriolic exchanges began again when a correspondent identifying himself as "A.S., Daly Municipality, Manitoba," wrote to the *Farmer's Advocate* (Feb. 5, 1900, p. 60) saying that he had no use for Clydesdales. "I consider them too soft for Manitoba," he said and then went on to explain why he wanted Percherons. A reply came from "Jas. M., Pipestone" *(Farmer's Advocate,* May 21, 1900, p. 270), delivering an elementary lecture on draft horse type and reminding all that "Feet and legs are the most important part of the horse, for, with good feet and legs, even though the body is a little plain, you have a good useful beast; but a model body with poor feet and legs, and you have what I call a good-looking 'nothing.' . . . I really think the Clydesdales — straight-legged, clean-boned, and with good action — are what we want." In other words, farmers want or should want Clydesdales.

For Percherons, the best chance to advance their cause came in 1903 when the breed was recognized with showring classes at both the Winnipeg and Brandon exhibitions. At Winnipeg, where the continuing popularity of the Scottish breed was attested by the eleven mature stallions coming together in the first class, the Percheron entry was unimpressive. An editor *(Farmer's Advocate,* Aug. 5, 1903, p. 812) reported the Percheron exhibit as "scarcely sufficient to justify its continuation. There is no question," he added, "but that good Percheron horses are being bred but the best do not appear to be finding their way to this country." It was part of that editor's continuing warning for horsemen to be on their guard against "fakers" from the south, offering "horses of a breed with which Canadian farmers are not familiar, asking from syndicates three or four prices, and giving all sorts of unreasonable guarantees."

Of the two mature Percheron stallions and two three-year-olds exhibited, the judge, Robert Ness from Eastern Canada, said, "a poor lot," and then awarded the breed championship to the winning two-year-old, a horse purchased by a Dauphin syndicate at a price said to be "about $4,000."

At the Brandon Exhibition a few days later, the Percheron display was neither bigger nor better. A stallion called "Archibald," shown by the Brandon Hills Syndicate, was the only entry in the mature class and two representatives appeared for the three-year-old class, one of them becoming the champion. Nobody was becoming very excited about that initial public appearance of Percherons in a notoriously strong Clydesdale area, but regardless of derogatory remarks, published and unpublished, the massive frames and comparatively easy-going characteristics began to win the interest of many men on the land. And having accepted the Percheron and then the Belgian, they were ready to argue more determinedly than ever with those belligerent supporters of Clydesdales.

Some of the most bitter differences arose at local fairs where much of the show-ring competition was in interbreed classes. The sections for grade horses brought together animals bearing the characteristics of different breeds, and the role of judge took on a new occupational danger. The Scottish horsemen expected qualified judges to attach an overriding importance to quality in feet and legs and elevate the sons and daughters of Clydesdale stallions to winning positions. With no less determination, men of the "rebel group" were sure that any judge who failed to be

Clydesdale stallions in the show ring at Brandon, Manitoba, 1906.

guided by the powerful bodies and obvious utility in the offspring from Percheron and Belgian sires was prejudiced and unfit for the tasks of adjudication. Depending upon the distribution of awards, the judge was branded by the ringside observers as "a Clyde man," or "a Percheron man." As such, he was praised for good judgment by one group and damned by the other.

So strong was the feeling in some communities that friends of the Clydesdale breed sat or stood on one side of the judging ring and friends of the Percheron and the Belgian congregated on the other. When a half-bred Clydesdale colt or filly gained a first-prize ribbon, there was cheering from the side seating the MacLeans, MacEwans, and Campbells. When victory went to a black, gray, roan or chestnut showing its Percheron or Belgian breeding, shouts of approval came from the opposite benches, and the judge knew that whatever his decision, he would receive both commendation and criticism.

The keenest of rivalry between breeds was in classes for draft and agricultural mares and geldings shown with halter; and draft and agricultural teams in harness. In these, the Clydesdales, with stylish white markings and bold and snappy strides, continued to win most of the contest victories. In six-horse teams, for example, the Scottish breed had an almost unbroken record of winnings. But while the bonnie Clydesdales were continuing to dominate in the show ring, and Shires and Suffolks were disappearing from the Canadian scene, Percherons and Belgians were making fast friends back in farming communities where the only test of importance was in ability to do a day's work with a minimum of hardship and loss of weight. More and more men on the land were saying that Percherons and Belgians were "easy keepers" and the kind that could be entrusted most safely to inexperienced hired helpers. The result was that Percheron and Belgian popularity climbed to equal and then surpass that enjoyed by the Clydesdales.

By 1940, the number of purebred Percherons registered in Canada had passed the corresponding number for Clydesdales, and Belgians were gaining rapidly. Actual registrations for the year showed 865 Percherons, 786 Clydesdales, 420 Belgians, thirteen Suffolks and five Shires. Twenty-five years later, all the draft breeds were down in numbers registered, but the Belgian was the leader, followed by the Percheron and then the Clydesdale; the Suffolk and Shire, by this time, had disappeared from registration statistics.

Breed rivalry lasted for many years, and while horsemen were berating each other on trivialities, they did not seem to consider that their chief concern should have been the new competition in the form of motor power, soon to force all breeds of heavy horses into decline together.

Chapter 9

Power for the Pulleys

HORSES AND OXEN could lug plows and harrows and do it with complete satisfaction in those pre-tractor years, but where was the pioneer to find belt and gear power needed to drive grinders, lift water, and turn the wheels of threshing machines? In some parts of the world, men harnessed stream water to drive mill wheels and generate the power required to operate anything from buzz saws to flour mills. But under prairie conditions, most farmers did not see enough falling water to drive coffee grinders, to say nothing of threshing machines.

There was not much choice, but resourceful pioneers seized upon ancient techniques allowing for conversion of horse and ox power, or wind power, to the kind of force required to turn wheels and pulleys. No power-needy person could overlook the possibility of capturing the resource of wind, the way the Dutch had been doing successfully for more than a century. Every prairie dweller was familiar with the force which blew his hat away, flattened stooks of grain, and generated dust storms and winter blizzards. That force was partially harnessed to serve farm needs, but even on the Prairies, a person could not depend upon wind to blow when wanted and men turned to treadmills and power sweeps, both of which would take their driving impulse from the weight or muscles of horses and oxen. Even dogs were used to keep small treadmills in motion.

A windmill was the pioneer among all engine-like devices in the Canadian West, the first one having been set up for operation in the Selkirk Settlement about 1825. If the Red River colonists had been more mechanical in aptitude, they might have enjoyed the benefit of wind power some ten years earlier, when Lord Selkirk sent the mill from England. But bewildered settlers, surveying the scores of metal parts laid out for assembly, concluded the problem to be altogether too complex for them and sent the dismantled monster back to England to be assembled or partly assembled for them. After almost a decade, the windmill was shipped again by sailing vessel—its third crossing of the Atlantic—and again transported from York Factory to Fort Garry by canoe. This time, the mill was accompanied by a Scottish expert who understood all the fearful intricacies, and the effort was crowned with success, except for the accumulated and embarrassing cost, at least £1,500. The windmill was sold to a Mr. Logan, and it gave long service as Logan's Mill, grinding wheat and displacing the hand power employed previously to turn the old stone querns.

Although windmills were the first power machines in Rupert's Land and continued to serve even after the horse-driven power sweeps and treadmills were relegated to the museum, there was a period in which sweeps and treadmills were first in favor. Horse-driven power sweeps were being used for threshing in Upper Canada at least as early as 1845. American-born Daniel Massey, who became a successful farmer near Cobourg, imported one of the first threshing machines and a power sweep with which to drive it about that time. In the machine shop and foundry Massey started beside Lake Ontario, he may have been the first Canadian to make sweeps for sale to farmers trying to increase their threshing efficiency. In the very next year, 1848, locally-made sweeps were exhibited at the Provincial Exhibition at Cobourg and the awkward contrivances, each with four radiating arms or bars to which the horses were hitched to travel in unending circles, became familiar objects.

Within the next few years, another maker of horse-driven power sweeps, William H. Verity, moved from Buffalo to settle in the western part of Upper Canada. He was the young Englishman who crossed the Atlantic on the maiden voyage of one of the first steamships and, arriving at New York, married the girl he had fallen in love with during the journey. Soon after, the young couple followed the girl's parents to settle in Canada. In setting out to make machines, Verity's first task was to fashion the necessary tools for plant operation, among them a power sweep with which to drive a lathe, a drill, and a giant bellows for a furnace. One of his prize pieces was a huge press with a twenty-foot hand lever for shaping hot moldboards for plows. And along with plows, stoves, sewing machines, and sugar kettles, Verity was turning out power sweeps for sale to anybody choosing to do his threshing by machine instead of flail.

Almost invariably, a sweep followed a threshing machine into the farmer's possession. In the new province of Manitoba, the man who imported a threshing machine

from St. Paul, Minnesota, either imported a four-horse sweep or contrived to make one. Manitoba farmers saw the first threshing machine driven by horsepower about 1875. In 1878, while the West was still without a railroad connection with the East, a thresher and sweep outfit was hauled from Winnipeg to Battleford, to the order of the Lieutenant-Governor of the Territories.

Four horses hitched to the long arms of a sweep could make a small threshing machine hum, but the sweep did not escape criticism. It was awkward to move and took too much room to be used inside. Worst of all, it was hard on the animals required to labor through the continuous circles to keep it in motion. It was an assignment that fell to horses rather than oxen because the cattle were supposed to be susceptible to dizziness and were honorably excused. It was one of the rare occasions when oxen qualified for favor.

Then came the treadmill, built like an escalator with its endless belt or treads moving downward under the weight of the animal or animals toiling ever upward on it. It had its period of popularity. Those who fancied the treadmill or tread power could show that a ton or two tons of horses or other animals used on it could transmit more power to a pulley than the same weight of horses hitched to the arms of a sweep.

Even before they were adopted by agriculture, treadmills were used in English prisons as hard-labor instruments. In their original form, the mills consisted of large wheels or cylinders furnished with steps on their perimeters. As a prisoner placed his weight on a step, steadying himself with the help of a handrail, the wheel revolved, and in some instances, the power generated was put to use in grinding grain. These prison mills existed as a means of penal discipline until the beginning of the twentieth century, and by that time, their counterparts were reaching their peak in popularity on Canadian farms.

If, the power sweep was hard on horses, the treadmill was no better and had the added disadvantage of being potentially dangerous. If the belt driving a threshing or a grinding machine broke or came off its pulley at a moment when the operator could not apply the brake at once, the tread on which the working animals walked, would suddenly revolve freely, leaving the unfortunate animals on it with nothing but the most treacherous footing. In panic, horses would flounder, sometimes breaking legs and necessitating destruction.

But when one of the agricultural magazines invited men on the land to report their experience with power machines, the majority of those replying showed a preference for the treadmill. (*Farmer's Advocate*, May 6, 1901, p. 266.) One

Threshing with flails, (page 33).

Even on the Prairies, the wind could not be depended upon to blow whenever the farmer needed power, so he turned to treadmills and power sweeps.

Power sweep (below).

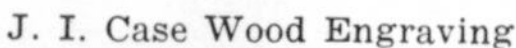
J. I. Case Wood Engraving

of the more philosophical responses came from Alex McLay, Horse Hills, Alberta, and was intended to show how the author's favorite power mill could be a means of keeping boys on the farm. "The bucksaw, grindstone, churn, cream separator, fanning mill and pump have driven many a boy from the farm who otherwise would have stayed and followed the most honorable, most noble and healthy employment of man," he contended. If more farms had treadmills, more boys woud not want to leave.

The treadmill had everything in its favor, according to McLay. "It can be operated in a barn or other shelter, so that rain, cold or snowy days will not prevent the farmer from cutting feed, grinding, etc., just when he wants to. It requires no engineer, no fuel or water, and no boiler inspection. It has all the advantages of a steam engine without any of the danger of fire or explosion. It is ready for business as soon as the animals step on it. A horse or bull will furnish power for light work and exercise will do the bull more good than harm. Gasoline engines seem to be coming into favor but few use them in this section of the country, probably on account of gasoline being high in price."

McLay's remarks were soon challenged. In a subsequent issue of the magazine (June 5, 1901, p. 332), "John Canuck" had something to say. He was opposed to treadmills and believed that farmers should have more stationary steam engines. "I consider tread-power cruelty to animals," he contended, "and if Mr. McL. who is used to walking on level ground, would walk uphill for one day, he would have quite a different feeling at night. The ideal power for the farm is the windmill," the writer concluded and then chose to indulge in what must have seemed to readers as idle dreaming. Why not use windmills to drive electric generators and charge storage batteries? "The electricity could be used to light the farmer's house and barns, making him independent of the Standard Oil Co." And if the windmill could bring such independence, why not use electricity from the same windmills to heat farm houses, making the farmer independent of the "coal combines," and relieving him of the necessity of lining up "behind nineteen other teams, waiting for his turn to get to the coal car, as the writer has done, with the mercury approaching 20 below."

Nor could correspondent "John Canuck" get away with his condemnation of the treadmill. Along came James McDiarmid, Poplar Lake, Alberta, who found treadmills to be most serviceable and was not convinced that walking uphill was so detrimental for either horses or men. (*Farmer's Advocate*, Sept. 20, 1901, p. 592.) A treadmill would cost more than a sweep, he admitted, but it would

Mrs. R. C. Russell photo

develop "nearly double the power with the same animals." He could report a three-horse tread power threshing a thousand bushels of oats per day and cleaning them "fit for market." And the horses, weighing between 1,100 and 1,200 pounds each, actually gained weight while threshing was in progress. They suffered no cruelty. "They had no sore shoulders and no one was eternally whipping them up to their work." As for walking "uphill" as horses on treadmills were obliged to do to generate power, McDiarmid drew upon his own experiences when herding sheep in Scotland. "I would sooner walk all day on a modern tread power carrying my own weight than pull a load over muddy roads, up hill and down. Remember, horses don't always get level grades working on the farm or teaming. . . . I have herded sheep in the hills of Scotland and climbed them many a day, but never heard anyone say it was cruelty to make us do so. Mountainous countries have always developed the best specimens of men and women and history goes to prove that when they are called upon to fight for king and country, they could always lick the tar out of men who always walked on level ground. So what is required to develop good horses is the same treatment."

While most farmers were arguing about the relative merits of sweeps, treadmills, and windmills, and a few were trying stationary steam engines, some bold ones, like C. E. Ivens, of Wallace Municipality, Manitoba, were inquiring about the advantages in stationary gasoline engines. "There are some objections to the horse power," Ivens wrote. (*Farmer's Advocate,* Feb. 6, 1899, p. 60.) "It is hard work for horses; there is more time lost in moving and setting; the horses are liable to get tired and let the speed down, and you cannot thresh out of the stook because all the horses are on the horsepower. Now, I think a gasoline engine would be just the thing to run a separator like ours. . . . Who makes them and what do they cost? What would the gasoline cost in Manitoba, per gallon and per day for a 10-horse engine? Will they stand cold weather out of doors? Does it require much knowledge to run them and do they take much attention? Can the speed be easily regulated? Are they as liable to get out of order as the ordinary steam threshing engine?"

The editor found some answers: gasoline would cost thirty cents a gallon in Manitoba and consumption was likely to run about one gallon for every rated horsepower in a ten-hour day. Such engines might be hard to start in cold weather, but once started, they would run satisfactorily. And gasoline engines would call for less in mechanical skill than steam engines. The editor's answers were enough to create a lot of fresh interest in engines of the new kinds.

Chapter 10

Binders and Bicycles

Western Development Museum Photo

AFTER HUNDREDS OF YEARS with only minor changes in agricultural implements, farming entered an exciting period of inventiveness and mechanical advancement. Strange and wonderful monsters made from wood and iron and hauled by horses appeared in western wheat fields, and astonished spectators were heard to exclaim: "What is farming coming to?"

"There is the carriage plow on which the driver sits," the *Western World* of August, 1890, noted in recounting recent introductions. "There is the press drill that drops the seed and covers it, also the wonderful binder, the most astonishing of modern machines. Then there is the steam thresher that moves like a thing of life from one group of stacks to another, separating the grain from the straw and chaff in the most rapid manner and feeding itself with the refuse; then there is the great elevator with its well-arranged machines that by the aid of steam, receives the wheat from the farmers' sleighs, carries it to its destination in the proper bins and afterwards deposits the grain in the cars."

"What next?" the writer was asking seriously. Attempting to peer into the next twenty-five years, he believed he could see machines doing more of the work formerly done by men and horses, steam engines gaining favor, "fewer horses in proportion to the population," more attention to soil fertility, farm homes and tree plantations, completion of the Hudson Bay Railroad, and the immediate benefits of a shorter shipping route to the markets of Europe.

The writer's forecasts were debated fiercely when men of the soil met in general stores, the waiting rooms of livery stables, and farm kitchens. It was the idea of more machines and fewer horses that drew the principal opposition. Nobody could dispute the exciting advances in harvesting machinery. By 1890, the older districts of Manitoba had already witnessed all the evolutionary steps between the primitive sickle and flail used by pioneer settlers and the quite modern self-binders and threshing machines. The harvester-thresher combines were yet to come.

The production and acceptance of binders provided the best possible example of what improved machines could do to change farming practice. The Manitoba impact was revolutionary. The man with a sickle did not expect to harvest the crop from more than two or three acres; the one with a binder was ready to tackle a quarter section of grain. The first models of that "most astonishing modern machine" used wire for tying, and according to the *Daily Free Press* of August 19, 1878, about twenty were in operation in Manitoba in that year. "They are naturally objects of considerable curiosity wherever introduced," the paper's editor noted. "The other day the agent for the McCormick machine, Mr. R. T. Haslam, drove a representative of the Free Press to Mr. R. Tait's in St. James

Farmers bring their binders to a halt(left) for a short water break on the farm of Henry Schieler, just outside of Moose Jaw, in 1902.

The man with the sickle limited himself to two or three acres; the one with the binder was ready to tackle a quarter section of grain. The binder cut and tied the grain into sheaves with twine. Two or more men followed behind, as in the picture below, and built the sheaves into stooks.

Western Development Museum Photo

to see one in operation. . . . As is generally understood, the binding is done with fine soft wire. The sheaves were all nice and shapely and strong enough for all purposes."

Obviously, wire had its limitations. A knotter capable of tying with twine was invented, and the first twine binder was brought to Manitoba in 1881. One year later, a machine of the kind was taken to St. Albert, north of Edmonton, and farmers everywhere were showing interest. In 1884, Major William Bell of the famous Bell Farm at Indian Head, sent forty-five of the new binders to cut wheat in a big field; incidentally, suspending all operations for several hours to allow a party of overseas visitors arriving by train to inspect the machines and the 180 head of horses hitched to pull them. And Thomas Sandison, Brandon's biggest farm operator, had an apparent weakness for the new binders and started seventeen Massey-Harris machines in 1892. At the Sandison dispersion sale in the next year, thirty binders were listed for sale. Neighbors said it took a ton of oats and a ton and a half of hay per day to feed the Sandison horses at seeding and harvesting seasons.

Even the twine binder did not satisfy everybody. Men who recalled cutting with sickles and binding with straw, wondered why they could not have machines that would remove the necessity of buying both wire and twine. Western farmers reading the *Farmer's Advocate* of January, 1890, (p. 13) learned of an offer of $10,000 provided by the Illinois State Grange for a practical machine or attachment to bind grain with straw. About forty inventors from various states, Canada, and Scotland showed interest and one working model of full size was submitted. The committee found the machine easy to operate and apparently satisfactory and awarded the grand prize to it.

The introduction of binders brought unqualified approval from farmers, horsemen, editors, and others. Why not? Nobody was being hurt by the introduction of superior harvesting machines, and horses, as the primary source of farm power, remained unchallenged. If anything, the position of horses was strengthened rather than weakened. But what if, as some people speculated, the inventive genius which had revolutionized harvesting methods now turned to create self-propelled power units? Could steam, gasoline and electricity be harnessed to become useful and practical "work horses" in pulling plows and cultivators?

The professional horse dealers, who were the chief spokesmen and promoters for the industry, just laughed and repeated assuringly that nothing would ever displace the Clydesdales, Percherons, and Belgians on Canadian farms. Editors of farm magazines, depending very largely upon the advertising from horse breeders and dealers,

The bicycle made its appearance in Western Canada in the early 1880's. The type with a big wheel in front and a small wheel behind was commonly known as a "penny farthing."

T. R. Melville-Ness Photo

echoed the sentiment that horse raising and horse using would be unfailing, like the water flowing over Niagara Falls. But horsemen, at that very moment, were facing more troubles than anybody recognized. Revolutionary changes in sources of farm power—as revolutionary as those in binders—were nearer than the boldest people realized. And still nearer was depression in the horse industry, something which was almost entirely of the breeders' own making. And if that was not enough, there was the sudden popularity of a two-wheeled thing called a velocipede or a bicycle, soon to become the center of interest.

The concluding years of the nineteenth century proved that the horse trade, like any other facet of industry, could fall into the mire of depression. The buoyancy of twenty years led to overproduction, and prices as well as interest in breeding declined sharply. For farmers who decided against breeding as many mares as usual, it was merely a time of adjustment and not to be taken as loss of confidence in horses for farm power, but importers and dealers in stallions and other pedigreed stock took heavy losses as their business dropped seriously. For five or six years, very few breeders bought advertising and some turned to other occupational endeavors.

About the same time, those pesky bicycle things, which made horses want to run away, became suddenly popular, and some warnings were sounded: "Don't be sure the revolutionary changes made in harvesting machinery will not be duplicated in the form of traction engines and don't be sure the new bicycles will not force many horses off the roads forever."

Bicycles had their origin far back in history. An early form was a two-wheeled machine which the rider propelled by striking the ground with his feet. A notable advance came as late as 1839 when a Scottish blacksmith, Kirkpatrick Macmillan, of Dumfries, made a bicycle which could be driven by means of foot treadles. Anyway, the last decade of the nineteenth century, when horsemen were feeling the pinch of depression, was described as the Golden Age for Bicycles, and the League of American Wheelmen had memberships totaling close to 100,000.

It was not easy to imagine steam-powered or gasoline-powered tractors pulling plows back and forth on farm fields, but suddenly, the bicycle was a reality and many people who formerly rode or drove horses were seen traveling on their two-wheeled contraptions. A few bicycles with big wheels in front and small ones behind made their appearance in Western Canada in the early 1880's leading the *Winnipeg Weekly Times* of July 4, 1882, to declare: "The bicyclist upon the highway is a moving menace to the public peace. He frightens horses, runs down small boys and elderly females and so conducts himself that, in the opinion of the ablest jurist, it is justifiable to shoot him on sight."

The editor of the *Macleod Gazette,* showing less belligerence, tried to use the first bicycle in his community to win Territorial distinction. Norry Macleod was reported as having received a bicycle in May, 1885, and "hard at work learning to ride the critter." In the issue of March 9,

In the early 1900's the first cars made their way to the West. This picture, taken in downtown Saskatoon, shows one of the earliest motorcycles as well.

Leonard A. Hillyard Photo

1886, Norry Macleod was reported as making more bicycle history, having "started yesterday morning to ride to Lethbridge on his bicycle. The distance is about thirty miles and there are two rivers to cross. This is perhaps the first bicycle trip made in the Northwest."

By April, 1895, Moose Jaw could boast "thirteen wheels in town," and steps being taken to form a "Wheelman's Club." The editor of the *Moose Jaw Times*, a better booster than many of his contemporaries, wrote for the issue of June 7, 1895: "How far the bicycle will supersede the horse is hard to say, but there is no doubt that it is obtaining a hold in our West that is astonishing. Clergymen make their parish calls on the steed that tires not neither does it consume oats; doctors make sick calls; creditors make the oft repeated visit and young men and maidens tell the old, old story during the exhilarating spin in the gloaming on the whirling wheel. The West wants the bicycle. It was built for it. The only hindrance to its general adoption has been the first cost."

Following closely upon the bicycle rage were the first motorized road vehicles—cars and motorcycles—and they qualified for much publicity. With more talk about displacement of horses and ruin for horsemen, horse lovers welcomed the statement from the widely-known and widely-respected Alex Galbraith. As reported in the *Farmer's Advocate* of December 20, 1895, Galbraith gave his views about a recent race open to all motorized vehicles, which he called "motorcycles." Chicago newspapers, trying to promote the machines, offered $5,000 in prizes and obtained only two contestants for the first competition. "Of the two starters, one went puffing and swelling headlong into a ditch; the other went over the course at the rate in which an ordinary Shetland pony could have travelled it. The next race was arranged so that all could be ready and came off last Thursday—Thanksgiving Day. Six machines started but only two were able to make the journey—a short run of some 50 miles in all, on good roads in the suburbs of Chicago, and the winner came in blowing about 10 hours afterwards. Fancy the breakneck speed this machine must have gone to travel 50 miles in over 10 hours. Another motorcycle left New York during the recent Horse Show, enroute for Chicago, but the last half of the journey had to be made on board a freight train; no comment is necessary. Verily the so called 'horseless age' appears as distant as ever."

The moral expressed by the editor of the *Nor'-West Farmer*, September 5, 1901, was clear: "Bicycles and automobiles are fads at the present time." They could never take the place of horses, either in Canadian hearts or on Canadian roads.

Chapter 11

Toots from the Steamer

AS THE NINETEENTH CENTURY ended and the new one dawned, a man on the still-fresh soil of the West could buy a suit of clothes for $7.00, a coon coat for $45, a four-room house with two lots in Calgary for $600, a dozen pints of Dow's ale for $1.50 and a thirty-minute cure for heart disease for 35 cents. A woman could do about as well, being able to buy a pair of woolen stockings for 25 cents, fleece-lined drawers for 35 cents, button boots for $1.25, and a bottle of cure-all painkiller for 25 cents. For the person needing farm power, there were good teams of horses to be purchased for $250 and if a buyer was a gambler with sufficient cash or credit, he could consider a 20-horsepower steam tractor for about $2,000.

The provision of power was still a matter of major importance in farming circles while people in other walks of Canadian life were largely preoccupied with immigration, provincial rights for the Territories, and winning the South African war which was not going well for the British. Canada was recruiting young men who might be good at riding and shooting for a second contingent to fight the entrenched Boers, and scouring the country for suitable cavalry horses.

Homestead entries were increasing at an encouraging rate—6,689 in 1899 compared with 1,857 in 1896—but there was still an abundance of unoccupied land and immigration was seen as the only practical hope in developing this sparsely populated area, for which leaders wanted to gain provincial recognition. Hon. Clifford Sifton, as Minister of the Interior in Sir Wilfrid Laurier's Government, had embarked upon an unprecedented immigration program and was drawing thousands of hopeful people from many parts of the world. The 44,540 immigrants who landed in 1899 were more than double the number entering in 1897. Not all the immigrants were going straight to the homestead country; of the 41,927 persons who settled in Manitoba and the Northwest Territories in 1899, about half—20,364—came from beyond the Atlantic, 9,839 from the United States, and 11,724 from Ontario and other eastern provinces.

The immediate need was for hard-muscled men who would work the land, but how could anybody overlook the almost-equal need for girls who could become wives and homemakers? A promoter for a women's college which might train British girls to be useful helpmates for homesteaders had some sage advice (*Albertan,* Feb. 3, 1900): "Toughness is the first essential. Our climate is a hard one and the railway freight being heavy, it will not pay to import those classes which cannot be reasonably expected to stand our winters without expensive quarters. A competent authority should make an inspection to see that they are sound in wind and limb and preferably large rangy females with good bones should be selected."

For many districts in the West, the new century brought the first sounds and smells from those "iron horses" powered by steam or gasoline. Horsemen, who had survived a few years of depression, watched with renewed confidence and some amusement. The most spectacular of the innovations—and as seen by many as the most promising—was the massive steam tractor, a sort of dinosaur among mechanical monsters. Generally bought with borrowed money, it threatened to drag its owner into bankruptcy. As noted in homestead communities, there were two sure ways of "going broke": buying a "stud-horse" and buying a steam traction engine.

The engine was a climax development in a long succession of advances which began when James Watt, Scottish inventor, devised a motor with some of the features of a twentieth century steamer and patented it in 1769. Turbine-like engines using the force of a jet of steam on blades or wheels were made centuries earlier, but Watt was the great improver and brought such utility to the steam engine that it was the means of substantially advancing the Industrial Revolution. It was Watt who discovered the principle of double action—steam being admitted at both ends of the cylinder to drive the piston back as well as forward—and it was he who invented a governor to regulate speed.

Richard Trevithick, of England, was credited with the application of steam to move an engine on rails just

The first steam engines were stationary models, kept in barns or warehouses to power threshing separators. Often they were put into use at sawmills.

J. I. Case Wood Engraving

after 1800, but it was George and Robert Stephenson—father and son—who, in 1829, built the famous Rocket, a four-ton thing with 20 horsepower, to be driven at the fantastic speed of 13½ miles per hour.

Canadian farmers, long before they entertained any hope of using tractors, showed interest in steam as a force for stationary engines, something to perform belt work more efficiently and with much more convenience than did treadmills and horse-driven sweeps. The foremost need was for a threshing engine, and judging from the newspapers of pioneer years, the first in Manitoba was imported in 1874. According to a news item (*Daily Free Press, Winnipeg,* July 9, 1874): "The first steam thresher in the Province is now in the warehouse. It was imported by L. R. Bentley for Farquhar McLean, Portage la Prairie." The report was printed just one day after members of the North West Mounted Police with a cavalcade including 114 Red River carts, 73 wagons, 142 oxen and 310 horses, started from Fort Dufferin on the famous trek which was to take them to the site on the Oldman River where they would build Fort Macleod.

The pioneer press told, also, of the introduction of steam outfits in the Territories. "The first steam thresher for the Moose Jaw district arrived on Monday," the editor reported. (*Moose Jaw News,* Aug. 1, 1884.) "It was purchased by Battel Bros., through Gaunce and Turner, agents for Westbrook and Fairchild." The Edmonton paper (*Bulletin,* Sept. 26, 1885) reported three steam threshers in the district in 1885, and added: "The twelfth bushel or 7½ cents a bushel is what some of the threshing machines charge." And at Lethbridge, the first arrival was four years later, the newspaper report (*Lethbridge News,* Sept. 4, 1889) being that: "The first steam thresher for this district arrived here last night for C. O. Card, of Lee's Creek. It is a New Model from the Joseph Hall Manufacturing Co., Oshawa, and was ordered through Messrs. J. D. Sibbald and Co., of this place. The machine is complete throughout, having a 12-horse power engine and all the latest improvements, including a stacker and grain bagger."

A big percentage of those pioneer steam engines and threshers carried the Eagle trade mark of J. I. Case, a man whose contribution to threshing machinery was similar to that of Cyrus McCormick in harvesting equipment, and John Deere in plow improvement. Jerome I. Case was a New Yorker who went to Wisconsin in 1842 at the age of twenty-three, and soon thereafter founded a machine company which gained international fame for

The first J. I. Case portable steam engine was built in 1869, and known as Old Number One.

The Stevens, Turner and Burns, another portable steam engine, needed the guidance of horses to help it from place to place. One of the earliest models is now at rest in the Western Development Museum at Saskatoon after years of hard work.

J. I. Case Photo

the performance of its threshers and steam engines. In 1869, Case offered an 8-horsepower portable steam engine and an improved thresher bearing the name "Eclipse." It was the equipment combination in which he was determined to specialize. The engine burned wood or coal, but the response from the public was not immediately good. People were suspicious of steam, having heard about boilers in ships and locomotives blowing up and taking their attendants to death. Fires had been started by sparks from such engines, and why take needless risks, even if the machines did offer convenience and efficiency in threshing? There were still those old reliable sweeps or horsepowers with long levers or arms or sweeps radiating from the central hub or capstan and through which the pulling power of from two to twelve horses could be translated and transmitted by rods and gears to a thresher. But Case was reasoning that when steam engines could move under their own power, their appeal would be multiplied at once.

Hauling heavy engines with horses or oxen was a nuisance, and Case said it was not necessary. In 1855, American farmer Joe McCune had connected his portable steam engine to the truck wheels on which it was mounted to make it provide its own power for moving. This was followed by an effort on the part of Merritt and King of Battle Creek, Michigan, to manufacture self-propelled steam engines, but the company was short lived. Case was drafting plans and by 1876 had a steam tractor ready for the market and good enough to win a gold medal at Philadelphia and later at Paris. In the year after its introduction—the year in which the Blackfoot Treaty was signed beside the Bow River, also the year in which the first railroad locomotive, Countess of Dufferin, was brought to Manitoba—Case sold over a hundred of these machines, and before long some specimens of the kind were finding their way into the new farming districts of the Midwestern United States and Western Canada. Here was something which, in addition to threshing, could pull plows and other machines. A few people sensed the great potential.

A newspaper report (*Brandon Sun*, June 12, 1884) noted a Dakota plowing experiment in which a steam tractor "drew eight plows, turning a sod four inches thick as evenly and as well as could be done by horse power. The plowing was done at the rate of twenty-five acres a day and at a cost of $1 per acre." Concluding with a prophetic statement of opinion, the editor said: "It is probably only a question of a short time when horses will be put to other work and steam made to do the plowing in large wheat fields."

Although the Dakota story made first-class news, the editor seemed unaware that at least one such experiment had been conducted on the Canadian side of the border in the previous year. From Regina came the information (*Leader*, May 17, 1883) that: "The first steam plow in this country arrived here on Monday. It is capable of being run at the rate of four miles an hour. The plow is built on the most improved principles and is supplied with 8 oscillatory plows."

A Reeves "Canadian Special" steam engine, 32-120 horsepower. Built in 1912 primarily for plowing, it was able to handle as many as twelve 14-inch plows. When breaking prairie sod it traveled at about 2½ miles per hour. This one, used on the Scabry farm at Pense, Saskatchewan, weighs 38,000 pounds.

Western Development Museum Photo

Anything costing $2,000 was not likely to become commonplace in communities where fat steers brought no more than four cents a pound and eggs were fifteen cents a dozen. Even in 1889, the appearance of a steamer hauling a long line of equipment was enough to attract eager spectators. An outfit leaving the exhibition grounds at Winnipeg gave proof, and as the newspaper recorded it *(Daily Free Press,* July 27, 1889): "As the crowds began to wend their way from the agricultural grounds last night they were treated to a novel exhibition. A large Stevens, Turner and Burns traction engine started from that part of the grounds where the agricultural implements were exhibited and went down the street with apparent ease, taking with it no less than the following in procession: a portable steam threshing engine, two large separators, a hay rake, a wagon full of implements and another vehicle. Mounted on one of the separators was the 95th Battalion band who contributed music as the procession proceeded to the Smith and Sheriff implement warehouse."

Like awkward giants which did not know their own strength, the new tractors were slow and cumbersome. Rate of travel on roads and fields was little more than half the walking speed of a horse. Belching black smoke, they were among the early sources of pollution, but nobody cared about that. They seemed to have the muscle to pull anything likely to be hitched behind them, and the multiple plow gangs designed and manufactured for them weighed as much as some of the lightweight tractors which came later. A point in their favor: they were not noisy like the gasoline engines but their steam whistles could sound loud and shrill enough to carry a call for water or coal or wagons for miles. They held other advantages: they were practically theft-proof. While horse owners of those early years and car owners of later years had to guard against thieving, there is no record of steam tractors having been stolen. At maximum rate of travel, there was no hope of a thief getting far away during a night or during a day and a night. And the broad impact of the massive drive-wheels would leave tracks which anybody could follow.

On a straight furrow, the steamers were easy to steer but turning at the ends of fields was a different matter. Big turning space was needed, but at the usual plowing speed of two miles or two and one-quarter miles per hour, the engineer had ample time to wind the cast-iron steering wheel to take up the necessary slack of chain which, with the aid of vibrations and unevenness of ground, would send the front wheels in one direction or the other as desired. Operators fancied long fields and long furrows in order to minimize turning, which perhaps explained an error on a big

The giant steam engines lumbered over the Prairies, breaking soil at a greater rate than anyone had dreamed possible just a few short years before, often breaking as many as a dozen furrows at once.

A 110-horsepower Case steam engine around 1909. The whole family has turned out to lend a hand.

J. I. Case Photo

farm in central Saskatchewan where the engineer was directed to break a certain piece of prairie land and extended his furrows half a mile too far and broke up an adjoining quarter section owned by another party before the mistake was discovered.

Plowing gangs for steam tractors came in many sizes, ranging from 6-furrow units to those with 12 and 14 plows. A tractor drawing 14 plows, each cutting fourteen inches of furrow, was turning a swath of ground about one rod in width and thereby breaking or plowing two acres at each round of a half-mile field. It made striking contrast to the one acre per day accomplished by the man driving a pair of oxen and a walking plow.

The steam tractor and oxen had at least one characteristic in common: both moved at a slow pace and refused to hurry. But something faster was introduced for plowing in 1901: it was a big plowing gang with two sets of plows to be pulled by a cable taking its power from a steam engine placed at the end of the field. Only one set of plows could be used at a time and while the idle set was carried above the beam, the other set was ready for use on the under side. It was what in England was called the "round-about tackle." The essential feature about the implement was that one set of plows turned its furrows to the right, in the conventional way, while the other turned the furrows to the left. At the end of the field, instead of turning the plowing unit, it was necessary only to reverse the plows — change from right-hand moldboards to left-hand, or left-hand to right-hand—and start back along the last furrow.

The Winnipeg promoter said *(Nor'-West Farmer,* Sept. 20, 1901, p. 593): "Any farm engine can be used to drive the cable and thus a use found for the idle engines. . . . In a country where so many threshing engines are lying idle a great part of the year, it seems too bad that they cannot be utilized in some way to assist in working the land." Stationary engines as well as tractors could be used, and another advantage, plows could be drawn at a faster rate of speed. The Winnipeg distributor argued that an 8-furrow plow operated in this way could turn four acres an hour or forty acres in a ten-hour day. It presupposed rate of travel in excess of three and one-half miles per hour.

There is no record of the number of such plows brought to the western farms, but two of them were taken to Raymond, Alberta, by the big and colorful Ray Knight, for whom his village was named. The Knights from Utah came to what is now southern Alberta in 1900 and acquired large expanses of land for farming and ranching. It was Ray Knight who, in 1902, organized the first rodeo in Canada and staged it at Raymond. And the Knights were the people, who, drawing upon Utah experience, built a sugar factory at Raymond and embarked upon sugar beet production on the irrigated land in the area. Raymond Knight believed that beets needed deep cultivation and to achieve his purpose he ordered two of the big steam tractors and reversible plows with cable. Thereafter, neighbors were amused at seeing two 8-furrow plows moving briskly across Knight's fields without either attendants or tractors close to them. The sight was enough to make some travelers ask themselves if they were entirely sober. But the experiment proved only the folly of plowing to a depth of twelve or fourteen inches, and it failed to establish any practical advantage for the strange implement with sixteen plows, only eight of which it could use at any one time. Regardless of the result, however, the test served a purpose; it was one more of the many experiments which somebody in the new country had to conduct.

A big and costly steamer for plowing was not a proper tool for homesteaders or small farmers. If it had a place at all, it was on the big farms, like the Bell Farm at Indian Head, the Canadian Agricultural, Coal and Colonization Company farms scattered along the main line of the Canadian Pacific Railway, the Detchon Farm at Davidson, and the C. S. Noble Farms in southern Alberta. It was a matter of economics. The quarter-section farmers had trouble

An Avery undermounted steam engine pulls a 12-bottomed plow.

enough in financing a team of horses. The first cost of a tractor and plow was often greater than that of the small farm operator's investment in land. The dangers were made very clear by the number of farmers who signed notes to get the steamer and ultimately lost their land.

In addition to the financial hazards, there was the confusion that the ownership of a steam traction engine could bring to a man's life. "We enjoyed the peacefulness of farm living," said a farm wife, "until we bought that steamer monster." A working crew of at least four men was required to keep a steamer plowing — engineer, fireman, plowman, and tankman. And the owner, as fifth member of the working staff, was likely to be the busiest person of all, arranging for the purchase and delivery of fuel, locating water in needed amounts, finding or making repairs, and trying to keep the outfit running.

A 30-horsepower steam engine was expected to use 2,000 gallons of water per day, a ton of coal or a couple of cords of wood and fifty cents' worth of lubricating oil. Repairs were always needed, it seemed, and owners and engineers spent more Sundays at cleaning flues than they did at church attendance. If hauling eight plows, and enjoying good luck, an outfit might break or plow between twenty and twenty-five acres per day. If it were mired in mud, however, or held up for a repair from Winnipeg, it did not plow at all.

An owner who favored a Reeves tractor for plowing (L. F. Clement, *Farmer's Advocate,* June 6, 1906, p. 860) estimated his daily costs at twenty-eight dollars and accounted for the total with the following charges:

Straw or coal team, man and board	$ 5.00
Tank team, man and board	5.00
Engineer and board	4.50
Fireman and board	2.50
Plowman and board	2.50
Wages for engine	6.00
Wear of 6 plows at 25 cents each	1.50
Oil and grease	1.00
	$28.00

To small landowners, the overhead and maintenance on a steam outfit seemed frightening, but when steamers could be kept going on large farms, without breakdowns and delays, the costs on an acre basis were not excessive. Many users were satisfied with the results. T. W. Green, of the Moose Jaw district *(Farmer's Advocate,* March 20, 1903), was keeping his 30-horsepower Case tractor busy most of the summer in 1903, pulling seven plows in breaking, eight in backsetting and nine in stubble plowing. He was using five dollars' worth of Souris coal per day and breaking twenty acres. Such economy should have impressed the most frugal.

And not far away, A. and G. Mutch, of Lumsden, with a three-section farm and over 700 acres in crop, were plowing with a Scottish Clipper and a six-furrow plow. *(Farmer's Advocate,* October 20, 1902.) Although the Mutches were among Western Canada's best-known horsemen, they could see advantage in having and using the steam power because "more work can be accomplished during the time best suited to give surest results, whether it be in the form of killing weeds through summerfallowing at the right time . . . another advantage is that the acreage plowed per man is increased."

It could not be said that steam plowing outfits were ever very numerous, but such popularity as they did enjoy waned quickly after the outbreak of World War I. Smaller power units, within the economic grasp of more farming people, captured public interest. The twelve-furrow and fourteen-furrow plows were relegated to fence corners or sold for scrap metal, but the steam tractors which had pulled them gained a reprieve for strictly threshing purposes. For a few more years they would retain the reputation of being the best of all units in furnishing steady belt power for threshing western crops.

Chapter 12

The Itinerant Steam Thresher

FOR MANY YEARS, the month of September belonged to the threshermen. As huge steamers and separators moved into seas of stooked grain reaching to the horizon, farmers were very conscious of the seasonal pressures upon them; working hours would be long and tempers would be short. Farm women moaned at the thought of feeding big and ravenous crews of helpers. The whole pace of rural living was quickened. It was exhausting, yet threshing left some of the fondest of pioneer memories.

The threshing outfit at work was the central figure in many of the unforgettable rural scenes of that period. It was not uncommon to see five or six or more of the working outfits from one point of observation. Probably five out of six would be steam driven and identified at a distance by clouds of smoke from their straw-burning fireboxes; the odd one would be a single-cylinder gasoline unit, making more noise than all the others together.

The threshermen's steamer, filled with mechanical wonder and muscle, performed with the ease of a John L. Sullivan pushing a baby carriage. Its general appearance in operation — quiet, steady, and mighty — never ceased to rate as a public spectacle. It seemed to breathe scorn for the upstart gasoline engine making a deafening racket. And the separator, eating up sheaves as fast as two, three, or four men could feed it, and blowing straw and chaff and dust into a barn-size pile, was a proper companion. Now and then it groaned as if the mouthfuls were too big for its gullet, then resumed its normal hum, in orchestral harmony with the motor.

There was no doubt about it; the steamer on western farms reached the zenith of its glory as a threshing engine in the years immediately prior to World War I. In a sense, the first two decades of the twentieth century belonged to steam. It was not that the horsemen were conceding, or their position was in any way weakened, but steam tractors had indeed made a dramatic bid for plowing duties on big farms and been accepted almost unanimously as the best of all power for threshing.

It was a strange spell that those great steamers cast upon people working with them. Although they were the cause of nervous breakdowns and bankruptcies, the men who owned them found lasting affection for them, and those who were the engineers and commanded an extra dollar a day on the strength of a certificate testifying to some knowledge of how much pressure a boiler would stand before it blew up never lost their loyalty.

"You can have your noisy and smelly gas engines," said one who had been an operator. "I'll still take steam. It was a pleasure to hear that big thing purring like a cat having its belly rubbed, even when the boys at the feeder were trying to plug the cylinder. If old threshermen are allowed into Heaven, by gad, I hope there'll be a Case steamer there for them to tinker with. I cussed it lots of times but still I loved the thing and a man likes to think he'll have some old friends with him where he spends eternity."

Threshing machines with major improvements were making their appearance in the last years of the nineteenth century, and J. I. Case's all-steel model arrived amid controversy and direful predictions about the inability of metal to withstand separator vibrations, in 1904. Farmers at Portage la Prairie had an opportunity as early as 1889 to witness one of the first demonstrations of its kind, a thresher with mechanical band-cutter and self-feeder. (*Saskatchewan Herald,* June 19, 1889.) As reported, it was an Anderson band-cutter and self-feeder attached to a Macdonald and Braithwaite's Case separator. "A load of sheaves was placed on each side and as fast as two men could pitch the sheaves into it, it cut the bands and fed the grain into the separator. . . . The band-cutter and self-feeder will certainly revolutionize the threshing trade."

The first self-feeders, however, were far from satisfactory in service, and it was some years before separators were being bought with both feeder and blower attachments. One of the first in the prairie country was reported in 1896. (*Carberry Express,* July 16, 1896.) R. R. Danard was placing an order for a 20-horsepower John Abell compound steam traction engine and a 40 x 60 Advance separator with automatic bagger, self-feeder and "wind blower stacker," making it "the most powerful and complete threshing outfit ever shipped to Manitoba, and under the experienced man-

A 36-horsepower Case steel thresher, brought out in 1910. The first all-steel thresher was brought out by Case in 1904, and though it was met with ridicule, it was soon copied by all other manufacturers.

Western Development Museum Photo

Many of the prairie steamers were converted into straw burners, as there was a scarcity of wood and as coal was expensive. This Canadian-built American Abell engine had a special straw rack built on the back. The fireman stood on this platform with the load of straw and forked continuously to keep the 25-ton machine steaming.

Western Development Museum Photo

agement of Mr. Danard, . . . bound to give good results."

Steam was acknowledged to be the best for threshing, but should the outfit be a big one or a small one? Opinions differed. F. Bolton, with twenty-five years of threshing experience in Stanley Municipality, Manitoba, wrote to express disappointment in the trend to bigger and more expensive threshing machines. (*Farmer's Advocate,* Feb. 4, 1902.) He favored small threshers which could be operated by five men when stook threshing and four when threshing from stacks, but, he added sorrowfully, no machines of such size were being made and offered for sale. The craze at that time was for more and more size. It was the big machine that was winning public attention and it was the big machine that the manufacturer chose to make and sell. It was a sign of the times when George Lane, of Alberta, imported and used the biggest threshing outfit the wheat country had known.

George Lane who ran as many as 24,000 cattle and several hundred purebred Percheron horses on the Bar U Ranch, west of High River, did everything in a big way. When he added wheat production to his operation, it, too, was on a large scale. It was for his grain farm near Champion that he bought the most powerful steam tractor he could find and fitted it to drive two big threshing separators at the same time. The two threshing machines were set side by side but driven by separate belts from the powerful engine, made additionally distinctive by its upright boilers. With this arrangement of separators, teamsters and spike pitchers were obliged to feed from one side only of each thresher, but threshing capacity was not restricted. Ten teams hauled sheaves from field to machines and two spike pitchers and a teamster fed into each separator. It meant that six men pitched into two feeders continuously. Interested visitors came great distances to see George Lane's threshing monstrosity in action and speculate about its practicability. The fact was that it was not practical. It demonstrated the mighty power of steam and the capacity of George Lane's big engine; it also saved the wages of one engineer and one fireman, but such economies did not go far enough to offset the high capital investment and other grain growers profited by the lesson. Lane's oversized outfit became the subject for lively discussions, but it did not change any of the country-wide trends.

The editor of the *Farmer's Advocate* asked farmer George Kerr, of Rosedale Municipality in Manitoba, for his views and published the reply on March 5, 1902. Kerr could echo the popular sentiment. His experience led him to favor the big outfit, preferably a separator with 42-inch cylinder and 60-inch body and an engine big enough to handle it when working to capacity. Such an outfit would require "seven or eight stook teams with four good pitchers doing all they can stand. . . . An engine of about twenty horsepower will drive this size of separator fairly well and is about as heavy as it is safe to cross most of the bridges with. . . . An outfit like I have mentioned, with tanks, caboose, est., will cost between $3,500 and $4,000 and should average about 1800 bushels per day and I think should thresh for [between] 3 and 4 cents per bushel out of the stack and 4 and 5½ from the shock. Wages here have been from $30 to $40 per month, and teams from $2.50 to $3.00 per day. . . . I am strongly in favor of threshing from the stook, even with the late wet seasons."

To George Kerr, threshing with the new and expensive equipment was in the nature of a profession, a job for a specialist, and in concluding his advice to the editor, he added a hope that if and when Manitoba obtained an agricultural college, there would be one department set up to give instruction on the operation of steam threshers and their management to "get the best value out of a gang of men."

But how was the farmer with a quarter section or a half to gain the benefit of a big threshing outfit such as he had no hope of owning? There was the possibility of farmers forming syndicates to buy costly machines. The idea was carried out a few times. Thresherman George Kerr suggested that six farmers, each working not less than a half

More changes were made around 1895. The straw elevator was replaced by a wind-stacker, which blew the straw away from the machine into stacks. The "high-bagger" or "automatic bagger" was developed, which sent the grain through a long funnel into a nearby granary or wagon.

Western Development Museum Photos

One of the first big steam outfits in western Manitoba was a Minneapolis traction engine and a 44-inch separator, the largest made at that time, and equipped with a self-feeder and wind-stacker. This picture was taken on Alex MacEwan's farm near Brandon, Man. in 1899. In the buggy is the local minister, who happened along at just the right time to have his picture taken.

section, "club together to have one of their number get a machine and let the others make it worth his while. As soon as one neighbor has grain fit to thresh, let a start be made, giving each one a day or half a day." This way, the crew would be hired from the farms to be served and "if there is a break in the weather the men and teams can go home and do something else, and the thresher will not have a gang of 18 or 20 men to board while the grain is drying out."

The idea of a co-operative sounded well but it did not prove popular. The man with a big investment in steam tractor and separator could not afford to restrict his services to a few neighbors. He had to be free to thresh where he would obtain the best return. He had to be free to thresh for anybody whose work would allow maximum threshing and minimum moving. Long moves by night or day were terribly time consuming and costly. Consequently, most owners became itinerant threshermen and made reputations for aggressiveness, endurance, and hardiness. To keep his machine running and his men willing to work long hours, an owner needed both skill and diplomacy. He had to adjust to nights without sleep and meals at irregular hours — sometimes no meals at all. A strong constitution was a prerequisite.

Alex MacEwan, who had the first big steam outfit in western Manitoba — a 44-60 inch separator fitted with self-feeder and wind-stacker, and a Minneapolis traction engine of the return-flue type and carrying its smoke funnel at the rear end—pioneered in custom threshing around Brandon and experienced all the usual varieties of tribulation. Twenty-two or more hired workers followed that machine. Two men went with each of eight stook wagons and two additional men remained at the separator as spike pitchers. It meant that as many as six men might be pitching bundles into the feeder at one time. The engine had plenty of power and on one occasion when members of the crew became anxious to avoid the dining table of a particularly unsanitary bachelor farmer, they established a record by threshing a thousand bushels of wheat in one hour. No doubt a lot more grain went into the strawpile, making the unpopular homesteader pay dearly for his dirty kitchen and unappetizing fare.

In its first season, 1898, that MacEwan outfit operated for sixty days and threshed for twenty-one farmers. In addition to the cleared fields and fresh strawpiles the outfit left behind, there was a string of broken bridges, including the 18th Street Bridge spanning the Assiniboine River at Brandon. Repairing bridges proved to be a costly charge against the threshing business, and after the 18th Street misfortune, river crossings were effected by loading

This threshing scene was taken sometime before 1900. The steamer, a return-flue type, was one of the early traction models. Note the load of threshed grain in bags. The bagger stood on the ground and put 1½ bushels of wheat in each bag, then bags were loaded in a wagon and hauled to the granary, or if it was close enough, directly to the elevator.

Harvesting scene (far right), taken at St. Isadore de Bellevue in the Batoche area around 1895.

Western Development Museum Photo

tractor and separator on a flatcar at Brandon or Chater and dispatching by freight.

Moving, even from one farm to another, took too much valuable time. After attempting to organize field work so that the moves between farms might be made at night, owners carefully staked out a short route offering the least chance of the ten-ton outfit becoming mired in wet ground. Nothing was more helpless than a big steamer in the mud. Having selected the course to be followed, it was the proprietor's lowly task to walk ahead of the engine, carrying a kerosene lantern for such guidance as its dim light might throw for benefit of the engineer. Sometimes a fresh strawpile, destined for burning anyway, would be set afire at the appropriate moment to dispel at least a little of the darkness. Half a dozen burning strawpiles—not an uncommon sight at that time when wheat straw was considered as waste—could do considerable to change the character of an autumn night.

Crews assembled from neighboring farms were generally willing to accept inconvenience while those composed exclusively of itinerant workers could be expected to have one or two chronically disgruntled fellows who, if angered sufficiently, might throw a stone or wrench or pitchfork into the feeder—or even a box of matches.

Operators charged by the bushel, three cents per bushel of wheat threshed from the stack and five cents per bushel from the stooks being the usual rates in 1898. The owner's margin of profit was small, and a machine which was repeatedly breaking down could leave the owner with a crippling deficit. It was told in Manitoba that a special ward at the mental hospital was maintained for owners and separator men who "cracked up" under the strains of poor threshing seasons. Visitors to that ward related the cries from the unfortunate fellows, shouting to their engineers: "Shut her down; she's plugged again; shut the damned thing down."

Crews ranged from twelve to twenty-eight men. The ideal gang was one whose members believed they constituted the best threshing team in the country and wished to take every opportunity to prove it. But the crew was not without class distinction. Pay was related to rank. The engineer was the high-priced gentleman, the man of the hour, the envy of all other workers, and in the early years of the present century, received $3.50 per day. (*Farmer's Advocate*, April 5, 1902.) The separator man who knew all about lacing belts, finding obscure oil holes into which to squirt lubricant, and surviving in an atmosphere saturated with dust, drew the second biggest wage, $3.00 per day. Next came the spike pitchers, commanding $2.50 per day and finally, the lowly fireman, waterman, strawman, and teamsters, all bracketed at $1.60. Where teamsters furnished their own horses, the daily reward might be $4.00.

If he had a good machine and the water was not excessively high in alkali, the engineer was not particularly busy and found time to stand leisurely on the massive drive wheel at the right side, arms folded, watching operations very much as a field marshal might observe the progress of a battle from a position of safety. His most thrilling moment came when, with an audience of youthful spectators, he placed his hand on the throttle and felt the mechanical monster respond to his will. The youngsters agreed that he had a soft job. He was paid for what he knew. Boys wondered how one human being could know so much and confessed to ambitions that they would someday be qualified steam engineers and enjoy the prestige and premium wages going with the position.

But appearances could be deceiving, and the steam engineer who did not appear to be busy enough to justify the handsome wage of $3.50 per day had more on his mind than uninformed spectators would have imagined. The twenty-ton or twenty-five-ton machine for which he was responsible might appear as a "gentle giant," but he knew

Western Development Museum Photo

very well the hidden dangers where steam pressure had to be kept at 120 or 140 pounds. It was understandable that the pressure gauge would be watched closely, but the water glass, telling of the water level in the boiler, commanded the same kind of attention.

To let the water fall below the level of the crown sheet or top of the firebox was to invite the most serious consequences. Without water over it, that crown sheet would become red hot with the chance of blowing both the boiler and the engineer out of the wheat field. The good engineer was constantly watching his engine's moods and especially its water glass. When plowing downgrade and the rear part of the crown plate became exposed above the water line because of water rushing to the forward end, the engineer lost no time in pulling out of the furrow and turning his machine to an upgrade position until he could take on more water.

That good engineer was thinking about proper lubrication, watching for leaks, and considering the necessity of cleaning flues with the long-handled reamer and replacing leaking flues during night hours or on Sundays. At the end of the day he let his fire down, cleaned the ashpan, closed the steam valve and took on additional water for the next morning. He was the last man to leave the outfit at night.

Nobody received sympathy but the person who deserved it most was the fireman, the seemingly tireless fellow whose presence on the job was required long before daylight. When other workers were just emerging from their beds in sleeping cabooses and hay lofts, he was bucking straw into the engine's gluttonous firebox and asking himself why he had not used better judgment in his choice of occupation. To assure the sceptical ones that he was indeed attending to duty, he blew a long blast on the steam whistle at exactly five o'clock, at which time teamsters were supposed to have completed all breakfast chores and be ready for hitching.

Harvest fare was never elegant—and no wonder. Having twenty-five extra men for meals—with the constantly haunting danger of wet weather and long delays—was almost more than a woman could endure, but somehow the farm women coped with it unfailingly. Appetites were big and meals had to be ready on time, rain or shine. Food was not scarce because most farmers could draw upon home-grown potatoes, turnips, carrots, whole wheat for bread, butter, beef, and pork. Two or three neighbors might arrange to slaughter a pig and a steer for joint use and hope the fresh meat would not spoil before the threshers had consumed all. Most workers were "meat-and-potatoes men" who would not admit to a taste for cookies, but for those who desired dessert, the choice was between corn syrup and stewed prunes. If most decisions favored the prunes it was because of house flies, multiplying prodigiously at that season and totally unable to resist the lures of the syrup jug, where they came to horrible deaths.

But if rations prepared by farm women were humble, those created by bachelor farmers were infinitely worse, and threshermen, not normally hard to satisfy, willingly worked overtime to effect early escape. While apologizing for his complaint, one worker explained how it was only when his dog refused to eat the meat served that he proposed a culinary switch to beans. When some disenchanted men undertook to empty a teapot for a fresh start, hoping to improve the flavor of the beverage served, and found a dead mouse deep in the accumulations of time, the bachelor was offended at the intrusion and made it clear that as long as the men were drinking his tea, they would take it as he chose to prepare it.

Steam threshermen in parts of the United States formed union-like organizations in a few instances. Anything of the kind in Western Canada was more in the nature of a fraternity and came long after the steam threshing outfit was challenged and vanquished as an economic unit. The members were older men with sentiment and memories, men who remembered the steamer's role in one of the most exciting chapters in the history of western agriculture.

Chapter 13

With the Sound of Thunder

THE INTERNAL COMBUSTION ENGINE—or "infernal combustion engine" as its critics chose to call it—came upon the western scene with all the noise of thunder, and farm horses which had learned to live with the big but quiet steam engines saw no reason to restrain their runaway urges. Horsemen were known to drive six miles out of their way rather than expose their teams to the explosive sounds from a one-cylinder gasoline tractor.

Discovery of a motor using a fuel-air mixture to produce an expansive or explosive force upon a piston or turbine blade was much later than that of the steam engine. Moreover, discovery came very gradually over a long period of time. One of the gasoline engine's celebrated ancestors was a mechanism using gunpowder for fuel and designed by Huygens, a Dutch physicist, in 1680. In such a weird-looking specimen it would have been difficult to sense utility or a relationship with any internal combustion engine enjoying popular favor. Other inventors tried turpentine and coal gas to provide the desired explosive force, but the biggest advances came only after 1876 when the Otto engine was produced in Germany. Here the improvements were comparable to those James Watt discovered and patented in steam more than a hundred years earlier.

The German invention was a four-stroke engine with improved compression of the fuel mixture. and a better power return from the explosion. But the Otto engine was so thoroughly protected with patents that other interested designers were prevented from imitating it until the patents expired in 1890.

The steamer of that period continued to hold most of the advantages, having appeared earlier than the gasoline engine and won the reputation of being easier to start and easier to accommodate with fuel. Finding wood or coal for burning was easier than finding an expensive substance like gasoline, at least until wider discovery of petroleum changed the situation.

But steam engines were far from perfect too, and the promoters of the internal combustion motors knew it. Because they had to carry their furnaces and large amounts of water for their boilers, those steamers were extremely bulky and heavy, and costly to move. Tractors weighing fifteen or twenty tons were not uncommon, and a Daniel Best steamer made at Stockton, California, at about the beginning of the present century reached 80,000 pounds or forty tons. One of the problems in operating this monster, made for the Middle River Farming Company of California, was to prevent it from sinking in soft ground, and its makers equipped it with wood-covered drive wheels, each of which was nine feet in diameter and fifteen feet in width.

Strangely enough, the earliest gasoline tractors were built with excessive weight, also, as if to emulate the steamers they were designed to replace. The International Harvester Company's 45-horsepower Titan of 1910 weighed 19,000 pounds without fuel in its tanks, and the 25 Titan of 1911, which could serve as a road roller as well as a farm power plant, weighed 28,000 pounds. Even in their general appearance, some of the early gasoline tractors seemed to be designed to resemble steam units. Did manufacturers believe they could gain some measure of respectability and acceptability by presenting their gasoline tractors with the familiar lines of the older steam traction engines?

Changes and improvements came rapidly in 1890 and thereafter. Early in that year, a Vancouver man, George Taylor, was said to have designed and made a petroleum-fueled motor plow, behind which the operator walked and grasped the familiar handles of a walking plow, just as one of the first steam tractors made in the United States and patented by Owen Redmond, Rochester, New York, hauled six walking plows requiring the guidance of six men at the handles. Instead of having drive wheels, the Taylor machine was propelled by a rotary screw pressing on the ground, but in other ways it might have passed as the father of all garden tractors.

Two years later, John Froelich, of Iowa, described as a

International Harvester Mogul 45 horsepower, 1910 (top).

International Harvester Titan 20-25 horsepower, 1910-11 (center).

An early model of a Marshall Sons gas tractor (bottom), threshing in England around the turn of the century. The parts for these machines were manufactured in England, then shipped to Saskatoon, Saskatchewan, where they were assembled at what is now the Intercontinental Packers plant, for sale throughout North America.

Western Development Museum Photos

thresherman and well driller, mounted a gasoline engine on a steam tractor running gear, made some new gears and used the resulting self-propelled thing for threshing in his area. After threshing with this monstrosity for fifty days, he had demonstrated what might have been considered the first successful gasoline traction engine. With the encouragement of experience, Froelich, in 1893, started the Gasoline Traction Engine Co., of Waterloo, Iowa. From this industrial beginning came the well-known Waterloo Boy tractor, which was sold and used widely in the second decade of the century, and it, in turn, became the progenitor of a line of John Deere tractors.

J. I. Case, who performed distinguished service in the improvement of steam tractors and threshing machines—his first mechanical loves, died in December, 1891, but in the very next year, the company introduced a gasoline tractor which proved to be more of a novelty than an industrial success. It had two cylinders, and like many other tractors in that pioneer period, it had the appearance of a big toy made from unrelated spare parts. Its flywheel was as big in diameter as its drive wheel and most working parts were exposed to the weather and the admiring eyes of the man driving it. Nevertheless, it represented an important landmark, and as a premature form of farm tractor which had to be withdrawn from manufacture almost as soon

Daniel Best steamer hauls cut timber in 1894 lumber operation.

The first Case gas tractor, 1892 (top left).

Huber Manufacturing Co., of Ohio, gas tractor, 1898 (top right).

Hart-Parr gas tractor, 1903 (bottom left).

Benjamin Holt track-type tractor, 1904, one of the first of its kind (bottom right).

Powell Equipment Photo

as it appeared, it made a useful impression. According to a statement in a company catalogue: "While the tractor was used for threshing in different parts of Racine County, the carburetor and ignition devices of that day were far too crude to permit the machine to become a commercial success. Consequently, further development was postponed."

While Froelich and Case were demonstrating their pioneer tractor efforts, a German scientist, Rudolph Diesel, secured a patent on a method of utilizing a lower-grade and cheaper fuel; once heated, the motor would burn and operate on any of several fuels, even coal dust. It was the forerunner of the modern diesel tractor.

A succession of new makes and types during the next few years offered increasing hope for a practical alternative to steam, even though the questions about absolute superiority remained unsettled for many more years. William Deering and Company made a tractor with two cylinders in 1891, and McCormick and Company brought out a distinctive model in 1897. Then there was the Huber Manufacturing Company, of Ohio, with a gasoline tractor in 1898. Waterous Engine Company, St. Paul, Minnesota, was in the market in 1901, and Hart-Parr Company, of Charles City, Iowa, in 1903. C. W. Hart and C. H. Parr were classmates at the University of Wisconsin and following graduation, they embarked seriously upon the design of a two-cylinder gasoline tractor with 20-45 horsepower. In 1903 they produced and sold fifteen tractors and then saw their sales soar to make them rate among the leading makers on the continent for some years. Still the new kinds came. Massey-Harris Company, Racine, Wisconsin, had a tractor in 1902, and International Harvester Company began with a 10-horsepower gasoline tractor in 1906, the beginning of a long line of tractor models to gain prominence.

A track or caterpillar type of tractor bearing the name of its inventor, Benjamin Holt, of Stockton, California, made its appearance almost immediately after the beginning of the century. Wanted was something to carry heavy tractors and furnish traction on soft, peaty soils such as those found on the San Joaquin Delta, and the flexible steel track was found to give effective service. The "cat" or crawler was to prove its worth under many diverse conditions of peace and war, winter and summer, forest and desert

Those early gasoline tractors varied spectacularly in appearance, as they varied in efficiency. There was no such thing as a conventional type or shape, and makers experi-

J. I. Case Photo

U.S. Department of Agriculture Photo

Powell Equipment Photo

mented boldly. One thing the tractors had in common: All made loud noises, sounding more like the proverbial boiler factories than creations for the displacement of horses and steam engines. Governors for the control of speed worked on the hit-and-miss technique, suspending explosions by keeping the exhaust valves open so that atmospheric air instead of fuel mixture was drawn into the combustion chamber until the flywheel revolutions per minute dropped to the working level. In sound and performance, they were "bang-and-cough" engines as much as hit-and-miss.

One-cylinder gasoline engines, whether stationary or traction, might operate at speeds as low as 300 revolutions per minute and hence, needed heavy flywheels to carry over the compression strokes and stabilize the drive. The result was that when ignition was cut off and exhaust valves were open, the idling flywheel might continue to spin for minutes longer than the best in toy tops. As the one-cylinder engines gave rise to two twin-cylinder, two opposed-cylinders, four cylinders and even six cylinders, motor speed increased and power was much steadier.

When compared with the older steam traction engines, these new and noisy contraptions had something to offer in efficiency of operation, even though there was less than complete agreement on the point. Gasoline salesmen, naturally, argued that their traction engines could demonstrate an advantage in economy, while the loyal supporters of steam chose to believe the claim was nothing more than propaganda. A few points were clear, however, even before carefully-controlled tests were conducted. The gasoline tractors did not require as much weight and could use more of their power for drawbar purposes. Where a steamer rated 20-60—meaning only one-third as much drawbar power as belt power—the gasoline unit with similar belt power could rate 30-60; with less of its tonnage in firebricks and boiler steel, the gasoline tractor could deliver half of its motor power to pulling plows.

An increasing number of the new gasoline tractors, however, did not settle anything about relative efficiency and economy. Sentiment was a major factor when men made choices. The older threshermen had steam in their blood, so to speak. The hum of a steamer at threshing time was like good music in their ears, and placing a mighty steamer in proper alignment to the separator it was to drive was a favorite sport. The steamer enthusiasts worked hard and loved it. But more than sentiment was needed to save the steamers, and a change was coming.

Chapter 14

The Horseless Carriage

IT TOOK HORSES and horsemen a few years to become accustomed to bicycles, and then there came something far more hideous—the horseless carriages, bigger, faster, noisier, and smellier. Inventors, it seemed, were prepared to go to any length to torment farm horses and those who drove them. It was difficult to imagine these new and terrifying things putting good road horses out of business but they could certainly make life very miserable for them.

Drivers of nervous horses had unkind and unprintable words for the electric cars introduced to displace horse-cars on Winnipeg's Main Street in 1892; but streetcars confined to tracks in restricted areas would never be as objectionable as the autobuggies or automobiles which could roam all over the place and appear on the most unlikely trails to whip up runaway fever in otherwise docile farm horses.

Loyal horsemen were amused or angered, depending upon circumstances, but it was some time before they admitted to seeing the motor-driven vehicles as really serious threats to Standardbreds and Hackneys.

The first of the mechanical monstrosities of the road appeared in Winnipeg on June 14, 1901, the property of Prof. E. B. Kenrick, of St. John's College. It was a Knox car, a two-seater with a long steering handle which could be turned forward to be used as a connection for towing purposes. This pioneer car looked like a deformed buggy and sounded, when in motion, like a machine shop. Naturally, it became a leading object for contemptuous remarks along Portage Avenue and even in 1905 it was said to have as much novelty value as a two-headed calf. Among the questions asked was: How would a college professor have enough money to buy a thing like that? For several years it occupied a leading position each time Winnipeg staged a parade. When it needed repairs—which was often—it was towed to the nearest bicycle shop or blacksmith shop, there being no such conveniences as garages or service stations.

Regina people could point to a one-cylinder automobile in 1906, its owner being Gerald Spring Rice, and within a year, the local newspaper was calling for laws to regulate speed. If horses were prohibited from traveling over ten miles per hour on Regina streets, why should autobuggies not be subject to the same limitations?

The first horseless carriage in what is now Alberta was a Stanley Steamer, known also as a Locomobile. Having arrived upon the Calgary scene on August 8, 1903, its presence on Stephen Avenue made men and women gaze in wonder and exclaim: "What is this world coming to?" The owner was Billy Cochrane, rancher friend of Bob Edwards, and he drove the vehicle over foothills trails and ranges very much as he might have neckreined a saddle-horse. On its first appearance on the foothills ranch, according to rangeland lore, an unsuspecting cowboy, supposing it was a freak critter running away with the boss, pursued and tried to capture the thing with his lariat.

This pioneer car was sold to Charles Jackson, another well-known personality of southern Alberta, and finally came to rest as a precious antique, the property of Glenbow Foundation, in Calgary.

The next car in the Calgary area, described as a Rambler made in Wisconsin, was brought to the district in the spring of 1904. Its owner, John Prince, created local history by driving it from Calgary to Nanton — all fifty miles of the way — in five and one-half hours.

The first car for Edmonton was unloaded at Strathcona on May 25, 1904, and the *Bulletin* (May 26, 1904) reported: "The credit of bringing the first horseless carriage to Edmonton belongs to Mr. J. H. Morris, who on his return from Winnipeg last evening, brought a two-cylinder autocar. The new carriage created quite an excitement on Jasper Avenue . . . especially among the horses and small boys."

This four-passenger beauty, with low wheels and a top-heavy appearance, remained the only thing of its kind in the area for the remainder of that year, but two years later, the young province of Alberta had a total of forty-one

The first automobile in Alberta was this Stanley Steamer (page 58) brought into the province by W. E. Cochrane in 1902. It is now in the Glenbow Museum at Calgary.

One of the first cars in Saskatchewan (below) was this Cadillac owned by Mr. R. L. Myrick of Davidson. Mrs. Myrick was at the wheel in this picture, as the family went for a ride in 1905. The car is now in the Western Development Museum at Saskatoon.

automobiles, some of them being driven recklessly long distances. One of the noteworthy road expeditions was in 1906 *(Lethbridge Herald,* March 15, 1906), when an Edmonton driver, G. Corriveau, went over the 200-mile trail to Calgary in eleven and one-half hours to establish a record. Mr. Corriveau, the news of the day indicated, "sold the machine, a 29 horsepower, four-seated affair, to W. H. White of Calgary, and in company with his son, Mr. White and Mr. Lundy of Innisfail, made the trip to Calgary."

This was enough to outrank the one-hundred-mile trip from Battleford to Saskatoon made by F. E. Kerr "in his new automobile" in April of the previous year. *(Saskatoon Phoenix,* April 21, 1905.)

Interest was growing faster than a crop of Canada thistles. "Motor fever or automobiliousness is a disease which is becoming alarmingly prevalent," it was noted. As the conflict between road horses and cars became more evident, horsemen missed no opportunity to pour ridicule upon the machines. A poor defence seemed better than none. The editor of a farm paper *(Farmer's Advocate,* Sept. 22, 1904, p. 1265) knew he would win cheers from the majority of his advertisers when he wrote: "Automobiling is a fad of the rich, so far as the country roads are concerned. For the most part, they have no business upon them. Record-making is a craze. Machines are run at reckless and immoderate rates of speed. Horses are terrified, rigs are overturned, and occupants maimed or killed. Pedestrians, also, including children, have been seriously, if not fatally injured."

Being far from faultless, the new machines invited the sharp tongues of critics. Horsemen found mean satisfaction in pointing to the many mechanical failures, like those reported from a Winnipeg street *(Farmer's Advocate,* Sept. 21, 1903, p. 938): "The cussedness of an automobile was fully illustrated on Main Street on Saturday. A machine stopped near the depot, and an expert was sent to fix it. He came in another auto, and soon had the baulky one running. It was only a short time, though, for it stopped twice before reaching William Avenue. Here the expert made his third attempt, and when his work was over he got into his own machine, but it also refused to work."

The humorists proposed that every car on the road should be accompanied by a pair of horses and teamster for the purpose of rescuing the misguided motorist in times of trouble. Enterprising businessmen considered seriously the advisability of stabling horses at various points in a city, where they would be within convenient calling distance when the temperamental autocars became stalled. As the idea was advanced *(Farmer's Advocate,* Sept. 5, 1899), the horses would be kept harnessed and ready at all times, "and when the motor collapses, the millionaire owner will

telephone to the nearest station for help. Talk about the horseless age! Why, horses are just entering upon a new sphere of usefulness."

With the increase in cars, there was demand for laws to govern their use, and western lawmakers were being urged to copy the regulations adopted in Ontario where owners in 1904 were obliged to buy licenses at two dollars each and carry number plates, alarm bells or horns, and lamps for night driving. In cities, towns, and villages, motorists were forbidden to drive at more than ten miles per hour, and on outside roads the limit was fifteen miles per hour. A few designated routes were set apart for speeds exceeding those named, but drivers, of course, ventured onto them at their own risk.

Western horsemen had some ideas of their own about the rules needed to minimize the menace of automobiles on the roads. There might be difficulty in knowing when the horsemen were serious. Some of them, however, after noting that horses had a pre-emptory claim to the road argued that they should be accorded all the consideration entailed in the following rules:

1—When the driver of an autocar observed an approaching horse or team of horses, he had to stop offside and cover his machine with a tarpaulin painted to correspond with the scenery.

2—Any automobilist approaching a corner where he could not command full view of the crossroads, had

Glenbow Archives Photo

to stop not less than 100 yards from the intersection and toot his horn before proceeding.

3—Drivers exceeding the speed limit should be required to pay a fine of one dollar for every mile per hour the speed was in excess of ten.

4—If an automobile caused horses to run away, compensation to the horseman concerned should be $50 for the first mile the horses ran and $100 for the second mile.

Needless to say, the lawmakers of 1909 were not sufficiently impressed to adopt those rules. Whatever sympathies they may have held, they had no more desire to drastically discourage the newer means of road transportation than they would have had to prevent steam and gasoline engines from being tried out on western farms. Horses would just have to become accustomed to the frightening sights and sounds of the mechanical road monsters.

Many horse users could view the new contest between steel and horseflesh with detached interest, but breeders of pedigreed stock, both light and heavy breeds, were showing their first concern. They applauded when they heard about New York brewers who in 1904 adopted delivery by "automobile wagons," believing them to offer more in economy than the horses, and then, after a fair trial, returned to the horses as the best and cheapest means of doing their work. Likewise they cheered every time they heard the words of the editor of the *Farm And Ranch Review* (March, 1905) being repeated: "The horse has successfully survived the bicycle craze and now, when he promises to contest the field against the automobile with every prospect of winning out, western breeders had better cease worrying about the 'horseless age,' which will only precede the 'manless age' by a very short time."

They were nice words, but an event of 1909 was enough to confound the editor's prophecy and project automobiles to complete domination on roads, both urban and rural. It was the appearance in that year of Henry Ford's Model T, a low-priced car possessing simplicity of design and a rare suitability for farmers and others. Born in Michigan in 1863, Ford began experimenting with steam cars about 1890 and made his first gasoline car in 1895. In 1903 he organized his Ford Motor Company and set about to design something quite new, big enough for the family but small enough to be priced within the reach of anybody with average income.

The Model T of 1909, priced at about $850, f.o.b Detroit, was the first of more than 15,000,000 to be manufactured. A four-cylinder, 22-horsepower motor gave it a cruising speed of about thirty miles per hour.

Men related humorous stories about the "Tin Lizzie," exaggerated accounts of its versatility, and wrote limericks about its performance, but popularity did not waver. Even horsemen who refused to accept the inevitability of farm tractors were buying Model T's. It reached the point, according to a Saskatchewan agriculturist, that horses which would shy at meeting cars of other makes and models would pass a Model T as if it were at least half Clydesdale.

Chapter 15

The Voice of a Power Prophet, 1905

AGRICULTURAL COMMUNITIES never lacked in opinions. Sometimes there were shortages of facts. Workers at the early experimental farms and agricultural colleges were quick to search for reliable information about grains, grasses, and livestock but slow in recognizing the need for similar studies in tractor power and machines. For a few years, salesmen were left alone to direct public opinion concerning the merits of the various forms of farm power. The result was argument without supporting facts. Farmers became confused, and those seeking proof of the practicability of alternatives to horse power had to find it by costly experience.

Men selling machines could proclaim stirringly: Our forefathers plowed with oxen; our fathers plowed with horses but up-to-date farmers are not satisfied with primitive methods and are adopting steam." It proved nothing. Nor did it prove anything that Joseph Gurnon, of Melita, Manitoba, was "of an ingenious turn of mind" and conducted a successful experiment in plowing with three 2-furrow gang plows hitched behind his steam traction engine and managed to turn between fifteen and twenty acres a day. *(Nor'-West Farmer,* June 20, 1901.) Even Thomas Edison, the great inventor, could be suspected of wishful thinking when he spoke in 1902 about railways discarding steam locomotives and adopting electric motors within thirty years. *(Nor'-West Farmer,* Aug. 20, 1902.) What seemed even more reckless was his prophecy, made at the same time: "Electric automobiles will displace horses."

With very little exact information, every man was entitled to his opinion. It was increasingly clear that in matters of religion, politics, and. farm power, it was difficult for people to be impartial. Even more than they needed tractors, farmers needed information of a kind they might hope to get from knowledgeable men having nothing to sell. But where were the men who could and would speak objectively about the economics of farm power? Where were the qualified men who would give advice about power in the way Angus Mackay of Indian Head was giving it concerning field crops, or Dr. J. G. Rutherford was giving it about animal disease, or Christian Marker was talking about dairying, or Alex Galbraith was advising on horse breeding?

At last they might be heard, a few small voices speaking from understanding, one of them being that of A. Burness Greig, who lectured later at the new Manitoba Agricultural College and was the engineer in charge at the first Winnipeg Motor Contest in 1908. Employing an academic approach, he could see gasoline power emerging with net benefits over the more popular steam, and writing in 1905 *(Farmer's Advocate,* Nov. 29, 1905, p. 1739), he surprised farm readers with his convictions: "The use of gasoline as a power of propulsion will ere long be recognized as the most economical means of using expansive force for agricultural purposes. I am convinced that in the near future the gasoline engine . . . will prove its superiority over the steam engine."

It seemed like a strong statement for a man who was supposed to be impartial. Farmers would be hard to convince. They were still horsemen at heart. They could show some interest in traction engine power as adopted by certain big farms in Saskatchewan, Alberta, Montana, Kansas, Colorado, Oregon, California, Nebraska, and the Dakotas. A big steamer, running steadily, could plow four or five acres an hour, but who ever heard of one running steadily and who would doubt that the purchase of one would be the surest and fastest way to bankruptcy for the man operating a farm of average size? Nor was it easy to see how a one-lung, hit-and-miss gasoline tractor making deafening noises could be a better or safer investment.

But this man with chunky body, oval face, ample mustache, and a voice like that of a prophet was getting a hearing. Looking into the future, he said: "The gasoline will not only be the cheapest engine as regards first cost, but the cost of working will show considerably in its favor, as will its easy manipulation in the field and on the road."

These were seen as strong words for a man who was not trying to sell something, but Greig went on to explain

A busy Saskatchewan threshing scene using equipment from the Western Development Museum. This 25-75-horsepower J. I. Case steam engine is operating a large wooden Buffalo Pitts threshing machine. Both were originally purchased new in 1911.

Western Development Museum Photo

why he believed them. "As with steam engines, much depends upon the operator as to whether the engine gives satisfaction or otherwise. Provided the machine is sent out of the factory in good condition, there is no reason why it should not easily be maintained in that condition, for the operator has much less to attend to than in the case of the steam engine. There is no boiler to feed, water and pressure gauge to constantly watch in order that the required steam pressure is maintained, no clinkering, burning out of fire bars, or firing stacks and prairie from sparks, no bad language or loss of time waiting for the teamster with the tank—not to mention the daily expense of such an outfit—no melting out of safety plugs, no boiler to blow off and clean out, etc., but whilst Mr. Engineer is saved all these laborious operations in connection with the steam engine, he has more delicate machinery to deal with in the case of the gasoline engine."

Greig admitted that the gasoline tractor of 1905 was far from being perfect. It was still quite primitive, as his observations about batteries and "sparking plugs" would indicate, but he had confidence that improvements would be made quickly, especially in the ignition. "The battery," he declared, "is possibly the greatest drawback to the gasoline engine. Few men understand anything about it, whether wet or dry. . . . The sparking plugs should be kept thoroughly clean. . . . I am convinced that before a thoroughly reliable gas-propelled traction engine is produced — one that can be safely used in districts far removed from towns and villages — that the battery must be done away with. Such engines [without batteries] are now being manufactured in Europe." Greig's reference was to the diesel engine invented in Germany thirteen years earlier. He explained about a lamp being used to heat the vaporizer, "which can be readily done in from five to ten minutes. The lamp is then extinguished as there is no further need for it, inasmuch as the required heat in the vaporizer is kept up by the internal combustion."

Farmers, naturally, wanted to know more about costs in steam and gasoline traction engines, and Burness Greig had something to tell them. He admitted the absence of controlled tests with traction engines of the two types but believed he had the pertinent data anyway. "In connection with threshing," he conceded, "the gasoline engine does not show its advantages to such an extent as upon the road or for plowing purposes. Straw, which at present is looked upon as of no value, is generally in this country used with the steam engine, whereas with the gasoline engine the cost of the spirit varies from 25 to 30 cents per gallon and some 30 to 40 gallons per day are used. Taking the mean of these figures, viz., 35 gallons, at, say, 25 cents, the cost of gasoline per day would amount to $8.75. As against this, we have no fireman and no team and teamster for hauling water; and further, the engineer is enabled to lend a hand at other work, so that all his wages should not be chargeable to the engine expenses."

The $8.75 per day for gasoline was certainly a formidable charge against the internal combustion engine, but of this amount, Greig would immediately write off a total of $7.00 in lieu of wage savings. What remained, then, was a difference of $1.75 per day and this, he was sure, would be more than offset when other factors were considered; the cost of taking straw to the steamer, stoppages occasioned by loss of steam, and the danger of burning straw stacks and even separators from wayward sparks.

It was in plowing, however, that Greig saw the greatest advantages from the adoption of the gasoline traction engine. Straw could not be regarded as a practical fuel for steam tractors doing field work, and the enforced use of coal introduced a cash cost; a steam traction engine would consume between one and one and one-half tons of coal per day and at an average cost of six dollars per ton, the fuel charge was immediately between $7.00 and $8.00 per day. Greig admitted that no tests had been made with gasoline engines doing full days of plowing and he was not prepared to say how much gasoline would be consumed in doing the same amount of work as with the steamer. But, "as in the case of threshing, there is no fireman required, no team and teamster to haul water, and the engine being lighter for the horsepower developed, much less power is required for its propulsion over the land. Generally, I am convinced that the gasoline is by far more handy for manipulation than the steam engine, and certainly the wear and tear should be less."

This machinery prophet of 1905, speaking when the two new provinces of Saskatchewan and Alberta were being created, did not expect to see an immediate adoption of gasoline traction engines for field use but he was sure the change was coming. "Just wait and see," he intoned, "gasoline will furnish the farm power of the future."

Chapter 16

The Winnipeg Motor Competition, 1908

GASOLINE TRACTION ENGINES disturbing the peacefulness of rural scenes with increasing frequency were like noisy and brash youngsters showing improper respect for their steam-driven elders. If the heavy steamers were not tried and true, at least they were tried and that was more than anybody could claim for the gasoline-driven machines. The lighter weight of the latter had a strong appeal, but men on the land were not in a position to conduct experimental tests and no public institution, either north or south of the international boundary, had seen fit to undertake a program of evaluation.

"How do you know what to believe about traction engines?" farming people were asking. "Every manufacturer and salesman has a good story and horse breeders dismiss it all as propaganda. What is the truth?"

It was for the Winnipeg Industrial Exhibition, acting upon the urging of Burness Greig, to take the lead. Calgary had the honor in 1908 of staging the Dominion Exhibition and Brandon held the first full-scale Winter Fair, but no event of the year could claim as much lasting importance to the West and the agricultural community in its hemisphere aspect as the Light Agricultural Motor Competition conducted at Winnipeg. In number of entries, it was not particularly impressive, but as the first of its kind in the world, it was a landmark event in orderly testing.

Horsemen, crowding the ringside to watch the judging of big entries in Clydesdales and Percherons, hinted that the idea of bringing those mechanical monsters together for a huge public display was a breach of faith on the part of the Winnipeg Industrial Exhibition management. Horses, after all, had provided the best reason for holding fairs and exhibitions, and in the opinion of their supporters the inclusion of a motor competition was something close to heresy.

But while those friends of Clydesdales, Percherons, and Belgians were trying to hide their annoyance at the roar of engines entered in the first motor competition, repeating that steam and gasoline tractors were for a few gullible souls only, the exhibition management was giving direction to agricultural history, just as the G. H. Curtis airship, June Bug, was at that exact time making aviation history by flying a mile in a minute and forty-five seconds in the skies over New York.

The Winnipeg officials had considered carefully. They had taken stock of the sudden appearance of many new kinds of tractors in confusing shapes and sizes. Advertising claims were extravagant and often misleading. The need for more information upon which purchasers could rely was very evident. Prospective buyers wished they could see the various makes and models working side by side. Winnipeg accepted the challenge. In providing rules, judges, and a testing ground, the exhibition officials were offering to enlighten the farming people and at the same time, remind tractor manufacturers that they must be prepared to back their sales claims with performance and efficiency.

The competition, as announced, was open to the lighter types, but a light tractor by standards of the day could weigh up to seven tons. Whether intended or not, the weight limitation was enough to bar the steamers. As it turned out, one tractor burned kerosene; the others burned gasoline and no steam tractor was entered in the first Winnipeg Motor Competition.

Manufacturers anywhere in the world could enter, the understanding being that all entrants would be required to perform before judges and be scored by them. The adjudication would resemble the judging of horses where conformation, soundness, and action were considered and the best one would win.

Appointed to manage was the competition's most loyal and enthusiastic supporter, A. Burness Greig, one reason for success. The two judges named were William Cross, of the Canadian Pacific Railway, and A. R. Greig, an instructor at the Manitoba Agricultural College, later a professor at the University of Saskatchewan. Together, these men drew up a score card to guide them in determining which tractors possessed the greatest degree of suitability for farm use. With a possible score of 140, points were allotted for the following:

Fuel economy
Hauling capacity per horsepower
Distance traveled without replenishing gasoline or kerosene
Distance traveled without replenishing water
Turning
Protection of working parts

Accessibility of all parts
Traveling speed
Ease of handling
Clearance of working parts from the ground
Steadiness of running for belt power
Selling price, f.o.b. Winnipeg

Nine tractors were entered for the competitive tests; seven of them appeared and "weighed in" like prize fighters qualifying for combat. On Monday morning, with the sun shining to delight the most demanding exhibition manager, the tractors took to the testing courses laid out inside and beyond the grounds, to haul loaded wagons, plow tough Red River Valley sod, and expose every detail of design to the critical eyes of judges. Manufacturers brought their best engineers for the tests, and the Cockshutt Plow Company loaned plows and expert plow operators to insure uniformity in plowing equipment. It was the tractors which were on test, and any differences in plows should not have to be considered. Moreover, the Canadian company manufacturing plows was happy to have the opportunity of displaying its wares.

The test for hauling and general suitability in performing various farm tasks was the first item on the all-week program. Here the tractors were required to operate one at a time. The course, over rough ground, was inside the fences on two sides of the exhibition grounds. Wagons piled high with gravel furnished the loads, but the amount each engineer would attempt to haul was for himself to decide. The first tractor called, hitched to two loads weighing a total of 18,940 pounds but it was too much and one load was dropped. Another started with three wagons carrying 30,030 pounds and finished with two wagons.

Perhaps nobody expected the tractors of that period to operate long or far without accident or delay. Sixteen minutes were lost while a hot bearing was allowed to cool. One of the tractors broke its steering chain and hit the exhibition fence, leaving a fine gap through which small boys and others might enter the grounds without the necessity of facing gatekeepers and turnstiles. And still another tractor broke down and was unable to return to the competition. Such diverse disorders were all too typical of the tractors of the pioneer period. He had to be a courageous fellow who would totally rely upon one of them to do his farm work.

The men who planned the momentous trials seemed to have considered every contingency except weather, and as it happened, rains on the third day made it almost impossible for the heavy tractors to move in the extremely heavy Red River mud. For the plowing tests set for Wednesday, the tractors would be required to travel from the exhibition grounds to the McPhillips Street field, about two-thirds of a mile away, but with rain falling, the engineers were glad to accept a postponement. On Thursday morning, rain having ceased, the tractors were ordered to the field, but the problem of staying on the still-wet road proved too much for some of the units. As told by the *Manitoba Free Press* (July 17, 1908, p. 5): "The roads were in a fearful state and it is perfectly safe to say that the motors that travelled safely over them yesterday can go over, or rather through, any roads they are likely to encounter in the west." Only two of the tractors arrived at the plowing field without mishap; the others became mired or slid into ditches and had to be rescued.

Finally, all contestants were at the field and busily engaged in measuring their fuel, selecting land to be plowed, and hitching to plows for the two-hour tests. And in spite of bad roads and the threat of more rain, spectators were numerous. The Winnipeg officials were convinced of the soundness of their innovation, even though the field performance was far from faultless. Spectators spoke approvingly of the quality of the breaking in that heavy sodland, but some of the tractors continued to experience trouble. Two tractors broke down and returned to the contest after repairs. Another broke down and did not return. It looked like the "survival of the fittest." And when more rain fell, the mechanical brutes floundered in the gumbo mud like horses in a bog. Still the spectators lingered.

At the conclusion of the two-hour time allotment, the land plowed by each tractor outfit was measured, and the exact amount of fuel burned—kerosene in the case of the Marshall tractor from England—was computed. There remained the trying task of getting the tractors back to the exhibition grounds for the third and last phase of the competition; judges would study the working parts of each tractor and consider the ease with which they could be removed and replaced when necessary. And having gathered up their notes, the judges retired to compute the final scores.

When all the computations were completed, the first prize and gold medal was awarded to the Kinnard-Haines entry from Minneapolis, a 30-horsepower, 4-cylinder giant weighing 13,530 pounds, the heaviest tractor in the field. In the field test, it pulled 6 furrows, turned 3.2 acres in its allotted time, and consumed 20 pints of gasoline per acre. Its score which gave it the gold medal was 117.6 points.

Second prize and silver medal was won by the International Harvester Company with a 15-horsepower, 1-cylinder tractor weighing 9,920 pounds and scoring 117 points. The fact that the heaviest tractor in the field won the gold medal and the lightest tractor finishing the test won the silver only served to confuse those who were searching for a relationship between weight and efficiency. But there were the figures, and the total scores were less than one point apart. That silver medal winner pulled a 3-furrow gang, plowed 1.8 acres, and used 18.4 pints of gasoline per acre.

The third prize was won by the Marshall Sons and Co. entry, a 2-cylinder, 30-horsepower tractor from England, with weight of 10,680 pounds. It drew a 3-furrow plow, turned 1.5 acres, and used 38 pints of kerosene per acre, making a score of 108.3. A 40-horsepower International Harvester Co. tractor was fourth with score of 107.7; a 35-horsepower Transit Thresher Co. entry was fifth on a score of 103.3, and a 20-horsepower International Harvester Co. tractor was sixth with 101.5 points.

Prices had to be declared for public study, and for the winners the figures, f.o.b. Winnipeg, were $2,270 for the gold medal winner, $1,800 for the silver medal winner, and $2,700 for the tractor placing third.

Winnipeg Motor Competitions (from top to bottom):
International Harvester; Holt Caterpillar;
Rumely Oil Pull; International Harvester.

Press reporters gave "honorable mention" to a tractor which was disqualified from competition for being overweight but allowed to perform for demonstration only. It was the 22-horsepower Hart-Parr, pulling a seven-furrow plow. The *Manitoba Free Press* (July 17, 1908, p. 5) had a special word of tribute: "Although rated low, this engine drew the heaviest load on the field and did deep breaking that left very little to be desired. The company was the first to enter the market with a gas engine and years of varied experience have taught them the secrets of successful gas engine building."

Thus ended the world's first farm tractor competition and however much the horse breeders tried to ignore it, it was a contest of undisputed importance. That its importance was international as well as national was attested by the presence of representatives from abroad, including Lynn W. Ellis who was there expressly to observe on behalf of the United States' Department of Agriculture. It was all very flattering.

Summing up, the *Farmer's Advocate* (Aug. 5, 1908, p. 74) noted: "The Motor Test which the Winnipeg Industrial management made a part of the program of their exhibition this year attracted more attention perhaps than any other feature of the fair. . . . Up to now manufacturers have been content merely to display their goods at exhibitions and exhibition managers have simply permitted them to exhibit, no awards ever being made. . . . The motor contest at the Industrial amply demonstrated that manufacturers are not unwilling to enter their machines for such competitions as these. They went into the business with enthusiasm that carried the feature through to one of the most interesting and valuable conclusions that any exhibition feature was ever carried to at Winnipeg or anywhere else."

And from the same issue of the *Farmer's Advocate* which carried the results of the tractor competition (July 29, 1908, p. 43) readers learned about a course in steam and gasoline engineering, the first of its kind in Western Canada. "About thirty young men from all parts of the province gathered at the agricultural college on July 20th for the special short course in steam and gasoline engineering which Mr. A. R. Greig, instructor in mechanics and engineering is conducting. Prominent gasoline engine firms have loaned the college a number of their engines and the students are being instructed in handling and running them. Most of the men taking the work have already had considerable practical experience with steam and gasoline outfits. . . . It is understood that this course will be made an annual affair."

The noise of tractor engines was becoming louder and louder.

Chapter 17

A Bigger Show, 1909

THE RED RIVER mud clinging to the drive wheels of the 1908 winners was scarcely dry before the Winnipeg management was making plans for the second annual motor competition. Having shed all traces of modesty, the committee would call the next one the Farm Motor Competition of the World. After all, it was the first and was still the only one of its kind anywhere.

When the second event was staged in July, 1909, there were more tractors in the competition, steam tractors as well as gasoline, more curious spectators willing to face the risks created by mud bequeathed from prehistoric Lake Agassiz, and more official representatives from far-distant governmental departments, universities, and manufacturing concerns. Burness Greig and other men who pioneered the program were understandably jubilant.

And exhibitors in the horse barns were no less resentful and sulky at the very idea of returning to a competition which could detract from the glory of the draft breeds. While disagreeing about the merits of their favorite Clydesdales and Percherons, the horsemen could agree in their disdain for the cold, dead steel in those tractor things. The Clydesdale men, generally displaying bushy whiskers and Scottish accents, had a further disappointment when their breed champion, the five-year-old stallion, Lord Ardwall, by Baron's Pride and owned by Sir William Van Horne, was placed below the black Percheron two-year-old, Halifax, property of Colquhoun and Beattie, for the supreme championship in stallions. It was another departure from tradition in an area where Clydesdale quality, like the Ten Commandments, had rarely been challenged. But Lord Ardwall continued to be seen as a model for Clydesdale type, and Halifax added to his reputation when he was chosen to head the big band of purebreds at George Lane's Bar U Ranch in the Canadian Foothills.

Scottish spirit around the barns revived considerably, however, when a span of Clydesdales was requisitioned to extricate one of the big tractors from a muddy grave its powerful drive wheels had dug. "Something you can be damned sure you'll never live to see," one of the faithful remarked with evident glee, "is one of yon tractors pulling Clydes oot o' the mud."

But the Winnipeg officials were out to make more mechanical history and once again brought the best men available to help them. To supervise the tests, Prof. A. R. Greig was appointed; and to judge the various events, the management named Prof. E. Brydon-Jack, of the University of Manitoba; William Cross, formerly superintendent of motive power for the Canadian Pacific Railway and a judge in the previous year, and W. A. Duff, western manager for Canadian Westinghouse. Another official, Prof. J. B. Davidson, of Iowa State College, was appointed with the title of Advisory Judge.

The scale of points drawn for the guidance of the judges was changed from the previous year and was announced as follows:

Brake test	20	points
Plowing test	20	"
Protection of working parts	5	"
Variation of speed	10	"
Clearance of working parts	5	"
Price	10	"
Distance traveled without replenishing	10	"
Hauling test	15	"
Turning capabilities	5	"
Accessibility	10	"
Ease of manipulation	10	"
Steadiness of running	5	"
Design and construction	20	"
	145	points

The most noticeable change brought to the 1909 program was marked by the presence of steam tractors. Their elimination from the competition of the first year was not part of the plan or policy, but the adoption of the seven-ton weight limit on all tractor entries automatically barred the steamers, all of which were big ones. But there could be no mistake about public sentiment; the old steam tractors

The Case 20-40 gas tractor was the outstanding tractor of its class during the Winnipeg plowing contest of 1912.

J. I. Case Photo

had lots of friends, many of whom continued to believe their favorites would gain favor and importance in western agriculture. Men with affection for those steamer giants were deeply disappointed at their total absence from the 1908 field and even accused the Winnipeg officials of prejudice. Now, for the second annual motor competition, the massive steamers would have their chance to compete and move with the dignity of monarchs.

Altogether, there were four classes in the new program, three of them for gasoline tractors and one for steam. Most tractor entries were machines of United States manufacture; three were British in origin and none was Canadian. The only cheer for those who looked for an engine of strictly Canadian make was the report of a tractor soon to be built by the Gas Traction Co., of Winnipeg, and expected to be ready for the contest in the following year.

Some of the tractors carried trade names like Case, International Harvester, Rumely, Marshall, and Avery which remained familiar to Canadians for decades; others bore names soon to be forgotten.

Here, however, was perfect evidence that western ideals in tractors had not crystallized. Variability in the machines on public view was the most conspicuous feature of the show, almost bewildering. Of the twenty-two tractors entered, seventeen were internal combustion engines and five were steamers. Weight varied from 5,000 to 40,860 pounds, the lightest being a 20-horsepower gasoline tractor and the heaviest, a 90-horsepower steam tractor. Strange as it seemed, both the lightest tractor on the field and the heaviest carried the same manufacturer's name, Avery Company.

Among the gasoline tractors were those with single-cylinder motors, two-cylinder motors, three-cylinder motors and four-cylinder motors. And even drive wheels ranged widely in diameter, from 41 inches to exactly 8 feet. Traveling speeds went from 1½ miles per hour in the case of some of the heaviest units to a surprising 15 miles per hour for the smallest tractor in the competition. And prices ranged from $1,700 for a 20-horsepower International Harvester Co. gasoline outfit to $3,400 for a 60-horsepower Marshall Sons gasoline tractor, or from $3,250 for a 60-horsepower Marshall steamer to $4,050 for a 110-horsepower Case steamer.

If tractors were to achieve anything resembling standardization, they had far to go. Perhaps diversity was a useful feature at that early stage.

Again the principal interest was in the plowing tests where patient farmers followed the contesting outfits up and down the furrows, round after round. Their main concern was in proving reliability and economy. As noted

Kinnard-Haines gas tractor, (top), 45 horsepower, 1901.

International Harvester Mogul, 20 horsepower, single cylinder, 1908-09.

U.S. Department of Agriculture Photo

Western Development Museum Photo

by Burness Greig, Mr. Farmer was looking for "an engine that will keep moving day after day without stopping for breakdowns," also one which would not require the backing of "a coal mine or an oil well in order to keep it supplied with fuel. He wants ample power with endurance combined with economy."

This time the plows were supplied by two well-known manufacturers, Cockshutt Plow Co. and John Deere Plow Co., and the result led Burness Greig to say that both deserved gold medals for the excellence of work performed on the allotted working land, made especially difficult because it cut across and included both sod and previously-cultivated ground. The biggest plow on the field was a John Deere Co. combination consisting of 14 bottoms, each 14 inches in width. This was the big implement chosen for use by the 120-horsepower Rumely steamer which turned 4.23 acres of the mixed ground in 75 minutes and did it with a consumption of 580 pounds of coal. This, of course, was not as impressive as the stubble plowing record made at Brandon in the following week when a Gaar-Scott and Co. double-cylinder steam tractor pulling fourteen 14-inch plows, completed an acre in 7 minutes and 58 seconds. This would be close to 8 acres per hour.

When it was all over, the judges' scores showed the following as winners:

Class A, for gasoline tractors, 20 horsepower and under, brake test:
1st prize—Tractor No. 5, International Harvester Co., 20 horsepower, 115.4 points
2nd prize—Tractor No. 15, Avery Co., 18 horsepower, 106 points
3rd prize—Tractor No. 12, Marshall Sons Co., 20 horsepower, 100 points

Class B, for gasoline tractors, 20 to 30 horsepower:
1st prize—Tractor No. 7, International Harvester Co., 22 horsepower, 112.1 points
2nd prize—Tractor No. 6, Russell and Co., 26 horsepower, 106.8 points
3rd prize—Tractor No. 21, International Harvester Co., 25 horsepower, 106.5 points

Class C, for gasoline tractors, over 30 horsepower:
1st prize—Tractor No. 16, Kinnard-Haines Co., 45 horsepower, 109 points
2nd prize—Tractor No. 8, Marshall Sons Co., 58 horsepower, 102 points
3rd prize—Tractor No. 19, International Harvester Co., 32 horsepower, 100 points

Class D, for steam tractors:
1st prize—Tractor No. 1, J. I. Case Co., 121.3 points
2nd prize—Tractor No. 14. Russell and Co., 118.5 points
3rd prize—Tractor No. 20, Avery Co., 115.7 points

The International Harvester Co. seemed to emerge from the contests with special success, having entered eight gasoline tractors and qualified for awards at or near the top with four of them. The company's gold-medal winner in the gasoline division, its 1-cylinder, 20-horsepower winner in the light class, pulled a 3-furrow gang, plowed 1.09 acres in 75½ minutes and used 1½ gallons of gasoline per acre. And what must have impressed spectators following the results closely, it was priced the lowest of all the tractors in the field, $1,700, f.o.b. Winnipeg.

The top-scoring tractor among the steamers was the Case with a specified brake rating of 110 horsepower. It started the field test with 12 plows and finished with 11, having plowed 3.6 acres in 62 minutes and used 442 pounds of coal in doing it.

Winnipeg had mud, just as in the previous year, but in spite of obstacles over which nobody had control, the event was another triumph, leading the editor of the *Farm and Ranch Review* (Aug., 1909) to declare: "What was unanimously agreed to be the most interesting feature of the Winnipeg Exhibition of 1909, was the agricultural motor contest." Such an observation from an editor whose paper was regarded as one of the staunch supporters of the draft horse industry, seemed particularly significant.

Many of the tractors in the contests were shipped from Winnipeg to Brandon for what was to be the latter city's first competitive event of the kind. With the roar of

Marshall Sons & Co. gas tractor (top), 32-70 horsepower, 1911.

Avery steamer (center), 16 horsepower, 1902.

Case steamer performing on a ramp at a western exhibition.

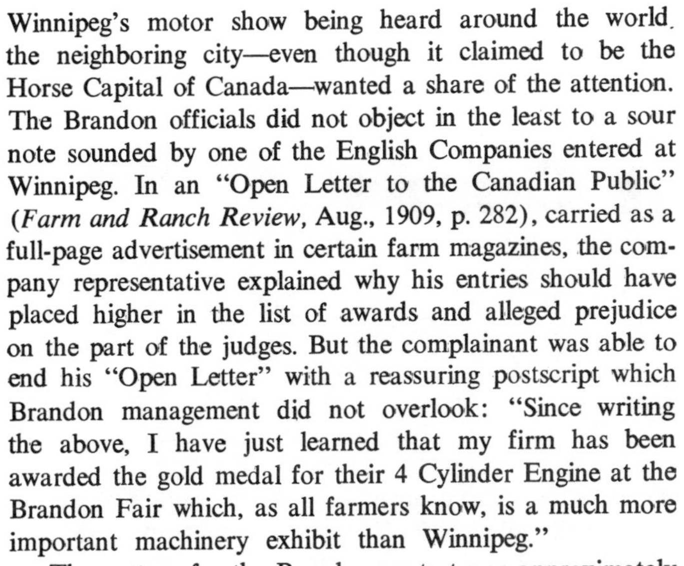

Winnipeg's motor show being heard around the world, the neighboring city—even though it claimed to be the Horse Capital of Canada—wanted a share of the attention. The Brandon officials did not object in the least to a sour note sounded by one of the English Companies entered at Winnipeg. In an "Open Letter to the Canadian Public" (*Farm and Ranch Review*, Aug., 1909, p. 282), carried as a full-page advertisement in certain farm magazines, the company representative explained why his entries should have placed higher in the list of awards and alleged prejudice on the part of the judges. But the complainant was able to end his "Open Letter" with a reassuring postscript which Brandon management did not overlook: "Since writing the above, I have just learned that my firm has been awarded the gold medal for their 4 Cylinder Engine at the Brandon Fair which, as all farmers know, is a much more important machinery exhibit than Winnipeg."

The pattern for the Brandon contest was approximately the same as at Winnipeg. But at Brandon, almost half the contesting machines were steamers, actually eight out of a total of seventeen.

When hauling capacity, plowing, economy in fuel, and mechanical design were considered and scored, an International Harvester Co. entry with a 20 horsepower rating won the sweepstakes in the gasoline engine section with a score of 121.4 out of a possible 135. And a massive Avery of the undermounted type won the corresponding distinction in steam tractors with a score of 139.58 out of a possible 145.

There was another noticeable difference at Brandon: what had been quiet disapproval on the part of horsemen at Winnipeg exhibition, blossomed into belligerency at Brandon. By what right did an exhibition management operating at the very heart of the draft horse breeding ground give these new-fangled luxuries operating on gasoline and coal such prominence? they were asking angrily. But regardless of wishful thinking on the part of exhibitors of heavy horses, breeders, importers, and dealers, the interest shown by farm operators was all the justification any exhibition board needed.

Nothing could rob Winnipeg of the distinction of having conducted the world's first farm tractor competition, but Winnipeg was no longer alone in conducting such events. For the next few years, tractor competitions were annual events of leading importance at Manitoba's two big exhibitions. Indeed, the contest for tractors remained an annual feature at Winnipeg right up to 1914, when directors announced discontinuance of the exhibition. They gave financial problems as the reason for the inability to carry on, but by that time the tractor business was entering a totally new phase.

Western Development Museum Photo

Stan Reynolds Photo

Western Producer Photo

Chapter 18

The Steamer's Last Gasps

THE BIG STEAMERS reached the peak of their glory in western fields during the first decade of the twentieth century. By 1910, signs of mechanical change were as clear as grain elevators on a prairie landscape. Winnipeg, in addition to having its annual motor competition in that year, held the first automobile contest, and the entries were judged very much as the tractor entries were adjudicated. The winner of the automobile championship, incidentally, was a two-cylinder machine carrying the name "Maytag."

It was at the same exhibition that many western people had the opportunity of seeing an airplane for the first time, even though this wonder of the age, brought from San Francisco by Eugene Ely, had trouble getting off the ground. After its repeated failures to fly satisfactorily, exasperated exhibition directors who were thinking about the initial payment made to the aviator served notice that there would be no further settlement unless he could make a better showing—in other words: "Fly in the air or fly the grounds."

Even the name used in describing the big power machines was being changed by common usage. What had been known as "traction engines"—both gasoline and steam—were becoming known as "tractors." And those machines powered with gasoline were stealing much of the limelight. The shift in public interest was unmistakable. The big steamers, as a force in farm fields, were dying—but not without a struggle.

Surprisingly, however, the number of steam tractors entered in the Winnipeg contests remained fairly constant. Spectators at Winnipeg saw 5 steam tractors in a field of 22 contesting entries in 1909; 6 out of 17 in 1910; 4 out of 30 in 1911; 4 out of 25 in 1912, and 6 out of 18 in 1913 when the Winnipeg motor contests were passing into history. Heavy rains during the show of that latter year, delaying and discouraging the field trials, demonstrated the vulnerability of such competitions. After another year, the Winnipeg Exhibition itself was suspending operations.

But there was no doubt: for the big steam outfits, the handwriting was on the wall, even though many of the old friends of steam refused to see it. The steamers were still the biggest, the strongest, and the steadiest sources of power for farm fields, and dinosaur qualities had their own undying appeal for the loyal few. One of the well-known manufacturers of gasoline tractors at that time, hoping to win public favor for his line of machines, adopted the slogan "Steady As Steam," an unintentional compliment to the tractors which were passing.

At Winnipeg in 1910, a 110-horsepower Case steamer hauling twelve 14-inch plow bottoms, turned 33.08 acres of sodland in eight hours and seventeen minutes, almost exactly four acres an hour. Who among western sodbusters doing his breaking at the tedious ox-power rate of an acre per day would not be impressed? The Case company was quick to point out that to pull the same number of plows at equivalent depth would require from 80 to 100 farm horses, and the cost would be much higher. "The cost of plowing by steam power," the company men pointed out (*Farmer's Advocate,* Sept. 14, 1916), "is easily 25 per cent less than by horse power. Not only that but an engine does not eat its head off between plowing seasons." To make the claim more convincing, the company spokesmen added that it costs $80 per year to provide feed and care for a workhorse, leading to the obvious conclusion that steam power is always the cheapest for farm purposes and "the 110 horsepower engine is undoubtedly the best engine to buy."

Men with ambition for big farm operations did not find it easy to escape the attractions of steam, even amid the rising popularity of gasoline tractors. Who with an eye for big and spectacular machines could ignore the odd-looking steam tractor with six rotary plows on an endless chain,

J. I. Case steam tractor, 110 horsepower, 1913.

Western Development Museum Photo

working two acres an hour at a cost said to be under a dollar an acre? This outfit, made at the Vulcan Iron Works, Winnipeg, and used on the farm of H. M. Powers, Elkhorn, moved at about half a mile an hour while the six revolving plows cut 33-foot-long furrows at right angles to the direction of the tractor's travel.

Who would not be impressed by the report of thirty-three acres of tough virgin sod being broken with a Reeves steamer drawing sixteen 14-inch breaking plows in its first half day of operation for William Rowse, of Hanley? And who would fail to marvel at the story about a big steam outfit at Semans, breaking a full quarter section of prairie land in twenty-four hours, even though the proof were hard to find?

With the rising interest in tractors powered by internal combustion engines, some of the old trade names carried on steamers were disappearing. The rivalry between manufacturers had been bitter, so bitter that at least one maker of steam engines refused to allow his machines to be shipped on the same trains with gasoline tractors, but now, certain companies were turning their production from steamers to tractors of the internal combustion type. By 1913, most of the steam tractors seen at Winnipeg and other western exhibitions carried the J. I. Case trademark. The company had done much to enliven the Winnipeg contests, and without its entries, the steam tractor classes in the competitions would have disappeared earlier.

The name of Merrill C. Meigs, Iowa-born engineer who could operate a steam tractor with professional skill and impart his enthusiasm for steam engines with similar skill, became almost synonymous with that of Case. He was the company's chief engineer and he would arrive days in advance of a contest, sleep beside his beloved tractor at nights to insure against vandalism, test the water to be used in the boilers by drinking it himself, and do spectacular things like driving one of the huge tractors up a 45-degree ramp, placing it on a teeter-totter, and closing the cover of a pocket watch hanging on a wall by easing the front of the fifteen-ton tractor against it. Canadian spectators loved his demonstrations, and he was responsible, in part at least, for delaying the complete loss of public interest in steam.

While some companies were abandoning steam tractors and going in exclusively for the manufacturing and selling of gasoline tractors, the Case company was diversifying, making and selling gasoline engines without breaking faith with steam. The distinguished founder of the company would have approved. At the 1913 Winnipeg contests, Case entries won in each of two classes for gasoline tractors, two classes for kerosene tractors, and all the classes for steam tractors. It was a notable record.

A giant steamer like this one could turn over more than four acres of virgin sod in an hour's work.

W. L. Jacobson Photo

By 1916, the Case company was one of the few makers of steam tractors remaining and still directing advertising at the farmers of Western Canada. "We are keeping our steam tractors right up to the minute, at the same time that we are manufacturing a full line of gas tractors," an advertisement (*Farmer's Advocate,* Feb. 16, 1916) announced, adding what a shrinking body of western farmers still believed: "Our belief is that steam in certain localities is and always will be the most efficient power."

At that time, the Case company was still making and offering steam tractors in seven sizes ranging up to the big one, the engineer's pride and joy, the 110-horsepower giant which had won a succession of plowing awards at Winnipeg and elsewhere and lorded it over competitory challengers of more moderate size.

It was all very well to remain loyal to old friends and old causes, but in spite of wishful thinking and grandeur in public displays, the steam tractor was an awkward and unwieldy monster and was going the way of whooping cranes and prairie dogs. Gasoline tractors of improved kinds were handier and more economical, and in a very few years, the huge multiple-plow gangs with 10, 12 and 14-moldboard bottoms were being relegated to fence corners, derelicts, there to remain until sold to some traveling dealers in scrap metal.

The big steam tractors which pulled the heavy plows were not abandoned immediately; because of acknowledged superiority for belt purposes, they were granted reprieve for a few years and brought out for use at threshing time each autumn. But the old steamer's place in threshing declined rather quickly, too. There were two reasons for the loss of its place in threshing. First, by the time most farmers had their own small gasoline tractors, they found it to their advantage to have their own small threshing separators and become less dependent upon the big itinerant outfits. And the second reason for the ultimate disappearance of the steamers from the threshing scenes originated in farm kitchens where the presiding women grew tired of peeling potatoes and making pies and washing up for the big crews of ravenous threshermen who followed the steam outfits. Nothing more was needed to tip the balance against the great steamers, and they were shipped away in reply to wartime calls for scrap iron, all except for the few to become installed with proper honor in western museums.

Nobody could rob them of the distinction of having triggered the agricultural revolution—just as stationary steam engines sparked the industrial revolution, but suddenly, the steam monsters were old and obsolete and were leaving the whole field of power farming to the newer and very different kind of tractors.

Chapter 19

A New Size and Shape

WESTERNERS WERE KNOWN to have a peculiar penchant for bigness—big farms, big steers, big horses, and big tractors. Manufacturers shared the obsession and even encouraged it. They could not forget the fine publicity gained from huge tractors like the Best steamer, used in California at the beginning of the century. That monster of the age, with its 82,000 gross pounds and drive-wheel diameter of nine feet, bred amazement and even a sort of hypnotism.

Tractor-minded people were accepting the principle of the internal combustion engine, gradually overcoming an earlier fear that it and its kind were so difficult to start, especially in cool weather, that prudent operators should leave motors running all night rather than face the danger of long delay in the morning. But if gasoline tractors were to compete successfully with the older and time-tested steam tractors, they, too, it seemed, would have to be big. The general idea was that if a man had the courage to depart from horses to buy a tractor, he might as well get a really big one. "If I'm going to spend my money for a gasoline tractor," one prairie man declared, "I'll buy with the idea that it's more economical to move a tractor and twelve plows for one mile than to lug a smaller tractor and three plows over four miles to turn the same amount of ground."

When three trainloads of Hart-Parr gasoline tractors came into Western Canada amid a good deal of fanfare in 1911, the machines, to be sure, were all big ones, and when two trainloads of Rumely tractors were delivered in 1912, huge size was still the most obvious characteristic. One of the best-known gasoline tractors of the period, especially popular on large grain farms on the Prairies, was the Big Four 30, an eight-plow unit with four-cylinder motor, a big appetite for gasoline, and drive wheels measuring eight feet in diameter. Made by the Gas Traction Co., of Minneapolis, it became a symbol of progress in the wheat country. Its cooling system held almost two barrels of water, and to start the engine, its operator used a torque bar and hoped fervently for the best.

Six of those Big Fours did all the field work, even to pulling binders to harvest the 5,120 acres of wheat and flax on the vast Weitzen Land and Agricultural Co. farm near Zealandia, in 1911. The *Farm and Ranch Review* (Jan. 20, 1912) carried a picture of four of the tractors at work in the harvest field, each pulling six 8-foot binders. With the illustration was the comment: "Without these Big Four 30s, it would be necessary to keep no less than 180 horses to do the drilling, discing, harvesting and other work." Surely this was an endorsement of gasoline tractors, especially big ones. But tractors and tractor ideals were changing faster than they had ever changed before.

Suddenly, tractors with familiar shapes but drastically dwarfed size made their appearance. The Waterloo Boy, with a two-cylinder engine and a power rating of 12-24 horsepower, appeared in 1912, looking very much like a miniature of certain well-known kinds. Not only was it readily received but it stood the test of usage very well. In the next year, farmers saw the Bull gasoline tractor, weighing only 3,000 pounds and selling for $400 at the factory. Then came two International Harvester Company tractors of the small order, the Mogul 8-16 horsepower, weighing 5,000 pounds and Titan 10-20, weighing 5,225 pounds.

But the most significant mechanical introduction of 1913 was the Wallis Cub, a tractor with a completely new concept in construction. Like some of its contemporaries, it was small, versatile, and apparently economical in performance, but in its "frameless" design, it was unique. It was the first of its kind using crankcase and transmission housing as a frame or foundation. It was as revolutionary as J. I. Case's all-steel threshing machine brought out ten years earlier and almost as controversial. But as time was to demonstrate, the construction principle allowing maxi-

Rumely oil pull, 30-60 horsepower, 1911.

T. R. Melville-Ness Photo

Hart-Parr gas tractor, 30-60 horsepower, 1910.

T. R. Melville-Ness Photo

mum power in relation to weight, and the enclosure of gears and working parts, was precisely what agriculture wanted for two-plow and three-plow tractors.

By 1916 there was no longer any doubt about it; the light-weight tractor was in style. And farmers across the West were being awakened to new interest. The main reason was World War I, foremost in Canadian thoughts at the time. With many young men in the armed forces, farm help was in seriously short supply and to make matters worse, the previous autumn had afforded only a short plowing season. Farmers needed more help or more field power in order to cope with the work facing them in 1916. Light tractors offered a possible solution and they were being purchased in increasing numbers. With new makes and models appearing, buyers had plenty of choice but in the absence of reliable information about comparative performance, they were largely at the mercy of salesmen making unsubstantiated claims. The Winnipeg Industrial Exhibition and the famous Winnipeg Motor Competition had ceased to exist, and it was for some other organization or exhibition to offer leadership. Winnipeg had withdrawn but Brandon, with its Provincial Exhibition and W. I. Smale as manager, was operating proudly with every evidence of survival and vigor. Sensing an opportunity to help the war effort and, at the same time, expand the Brandon Exhibition, the management announced Canada's First Light Tractor Plowing Demonstration for July 18, 19, and 20, 1916.

Conscious of Brandon's omnipotence in the realm of heavy horses, the directors chose to tread cautiously. They could not afford to offend the breeders of Clydesdales and Percherons and managed to couch their announcement in terms with which nobody could take exception: "Light tractors are being purchased by farmers of Western Canada in such numbers, and such vast sums of money are being tied up in this class of farm power machinery, that the matter is of considerable importance to Western Canada's agricultural situation." Still using what seemed like words of apology, the announcement continued: "The large demand for light tractors is no doubt due, to a great extent, to the labor shortage in the Canadian West. The farmer is trying in every way possible to reduce his hired help requirements to a minimum and the tractor appears to offer a solution to the problem. . . . Realizing all this, the Provincial Exhibition at Brandon has decided to lend every possible aid to the demonstration of light power farming machinery." And Manager Smale's diplomacy was successful, because it was the first program featuring tractors against which the breeders of purebred draft horses did not register objection.

Differing from the famous Winnipeg tractor performances, the Brandon one was entirely non-competitive. No awards were made, no medals given, no fuel or drawbar tests conducted, no engineers felt it necessary to sleep beside their engines in order to protect them from the destructive onslaught of competitors. Basically, it was an

Wallis Cub, 1913. A new concept in construction.

Gas Traction Co. Big Four, 1910 (bottom).

T. R. Melville-Ness Photos

International Harvester tractor, Titan 10-20, (left) 1914-1924.

International Harvester Mogul, single cylinder, (right) 1915.

Overland touring automobile, (top) 1911.

Ford touring car (center) 1933.

Maxwell roadster, (bottom) 1906.

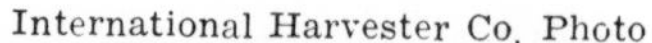
International Harvester Co. Photo

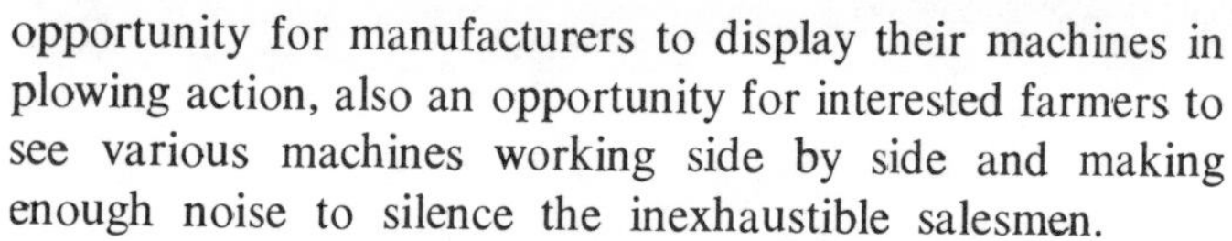

opportunity for manufacturers to display their machines in plowing action, also an opportunity for interested farmers to see various machines working side by side and making enough noise to silence the inexhaustible salesmen.

The demonstrations were conducted on a farm adjoining the exhibition grounds, a field which had not been plowed for two years. What the public announcement did not tell was the fact of the field having become badly infested with quack grass, making for very heavy plowing. But the quality of plowing was said to be high, and the quack grass roots only added an unauthorized test of tractor power.

Not only were visiting farmers afforded the chance of seeing many kinds of tractors at work, but for a fee of twenty-five cents per person, they could ride the short distance from the exhibition grounds to the site of plowing in an automobile. For many of the visitors, it was the first ride in one of the horseless carriages and the money seemed to be well spent. Automobile agents took the opportunity to conduct some timely advertising and when farmers buying a ride to the plowing demonstration inquired what one of these "power buggies" would cost, what they learned was not so shocking as they might have expected—an Overland touring car for $890, f.o.b. Toronto; a Maxwell touring car for $850, f.o.b. Windsor; a Briscoe for $825, f.o.b. Brockville, and a Ford touring car for $490, f.o.b. Ford, Ontario.

The essential point in the plowing demonstration rules was: "No tractor can be entered that pulls more than five plows." Needless to say, no steam engines were entered. It was the worst possible affront to the gasoline and steam giants, which had captured public attention in other years. But this was 1916, a year marking a new era in farm power.

Just as Manager Smale had anticipated, the First Light Tractor Plowing Demonstration was a huge success. Nineteen outfits entered by thirteen manufacturing and handling concerns took to the field to do series plowing on a one-mile furrow. Companies represented with one or more light tractors were: Emerson-Brantingham Implement Co.; Minneapolis Steel and Machinery Co.; Waterloo Gasoline Engine Co.; Hart-Parr Co.; Sawyer-Massey Co.; Grain Growers' Grain Co.; Goold, Shapley and Muir Ltd.; International Harvester Co.; Bull Tractor Co.; Canadian Avery Co.; J. D. Adshead Co.; J. I. Case Threshing Machine Co., and Marshall Sons and Co.

Two tractors operated with five-furrow plows, two with two-furrow plows, and all others with three-furrow and four-furrow gangs. And while no winners were declared and no trophies awarded, it was evident that the lightest of the "Light Tractors" were attracting the biggest share of spectator interest; the Happy Farmer, riding on three wheels and selling for $850 at Winnipeg; the two-plow Big Bull, with only one drive wheel and priced at $825, Winnipeg, or $875, Edmonton; the three-plow Waterloo Boy and the two-plow Mogul, in about the same price range.

In the commercial exhibit section of the exhibition grounds, completely removed from the plowing demonstration, a few steam tractors invited attention by the blowing of their shrill whistles and the climbing of plank ramps. Likewise, a few big gasoline tractors—too big to qualify for inclusion in the plowing demonstration—were making their bid for public interest. But theirs was a dying cause; 1916 was the first big year for the new shapes and sizes.

Reynolds Museum Photo

Western Development Museum Photo

Reynolds Museum Photo

Chapter 20

Demands Created by War

Western Development Museum Photo

THE PERIOD OF WORLD WAR I brought new dimensions to the tractor business. In farming communities there was a sudden burst of interest and manufacturers responded eagerly—in some cases, too eagerly.

When Brandon held its second Light Tractor Plowing Demonstration in 1917, visitors saw dozens of different makes and models—no two alike—and came away confused by the growing diversity of design. Manufacturers sensed an unprecedented opportunity to promote and sell two-plow and three-plow tractors for use on farms of medium or average size. The new challenge was one created by labor shortage and the wartime call for increased food production. Food, it was suggested over and over again, might win the war. Farmers stood ready to do their part but were seriously handicapped by the large number of able-bodied young workers entering the army. Old businessmen offered to help and women and girls responded by driving horses and working in the fields. Such assistance was appreciated, but it was not enough and farmers turned their thoughts to light tractors—the kind they might buy for the price of a four-horse or six-horse team—as the best single source of relief. Horses pulling field implements for sixteen or twenty miles a day were quite sufficient in normal times, but the circumstances of war demanded something which could handle bigger loads and could be worked for longer hours.

Farmers who had never before shown interest in tractors were making inquiries, and manufacturers were scrambling to capture public attention, mainly with low prices and novel designs. By the end of the war, nearly 200 North American firms were making and selling farm tractors and apparently finding a ready market for them because continental sales doubled every two years between 1913 and 1920. Tractors on United States' farms numbered 14,000 in 1913; 25,000 in 1915; 51,000 in 1917; 158,000 in 1919, and 246,000 in 1920. Increases on Western Canadian farms were, no doubt, at a similar rate.

Every manufacturer wanted a share of the booming business and many of the makers could not wait for proper performance tests. Understandably, the uncompromising tests of farm use served quickly to expose the poor ones

Bates Steel Mule, 13-30 horsepower, 1917 (page 76).

Detroit Rein Drive, 1915. The tractor was controlled by means of lines or reins, in a fashion similar to that of a horseman handling his team.

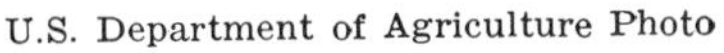
U.S. Department of Agriculture Photo

and most of them disappeared from the market. By 1927, only a dozen or so farm tractor firms were commanding any substantial degree of public attention, and by that time, farmer interests were shifting again, now toward slightly bigger power units.

Certainly, nobody seeing the new tractors in 1917 and 1918 could accuse manufacturers of any lack of imagination. Perhaps they were taking too many liberties in point of inventiveness, just as they were making too many claims about unproven machines. The tractor business was running slightly wild. Every time a farmer picked up an agricultural magazine, he saw new tractors being advertised as the Greatest Ever. Some of them might be untried misfits, with little more durability than a forkful of hay in a windstorm.

That tractor motors differed vastly was not surprising. Cylinder numbers varied. Some were horizontal, some vertical; some motors were of the high-speed kind, some were not. Even more conspicuous were the variations in shape and weight, and number and placement of road wheels. Some manufacturers continued to believe they needed 500 pounds of tractor weight for each rated horsepower, while others were going for lighter weights, even to 150 pounds per horsepower. Most manufacturers had turned to the two-plow and three-plow sizes which were currently popular, while a few were gambling on farm preferences swinging back to bigger power units.

Some of the unusual specimens of the time deserve review. The Moline Universal, introduced in 1915 and seen at Brandon in 1917, was a tractor-and-plow combination with plows attached on the underside and the two drive wheels at the front rather than at the rear. "Universal" meant that it was supposed to do anything workhorses could do. It had a 9-18 horsepower rating and was offered as a two-plow tractor. Resembling the Moline in placement of wheels —two drivers in front—were the Allis-Chalmers 6-12 horsepower model of the day, and the Cole Rein Drive, which had its operator sitting on a converted horse plow or other implement and steering with a pair of leather lines, just as he would have done if driving a span of Clydesdales.

Three-wheel tractors were quite common but wheel placement differed. The Big Bull, Happy Farmer and the Grain Growers' tractors were three-wheelers, each with a single wheel in front. Another three-wheel tractor, the Manitoba Universal, had one drive wheel at the rear and two small wheels in front. It was one of the very few Canadian-made tractors being offered at the time, an 8-16 horsepower unit made by the Universal Farm Tractor Co., of Winnipeg, and selling for $697 at the point of manufacture. Still a different wheel arrangement was seen in the

Bates Steel Mule with crawler track at the rear to do the driving and two small carrying wheels in front. "It's a regular mud-hen," makers claimed for the Steel Mule.

Still different in its wheels was the powerful Gray tractor. Instead of having the conventional drive wheels, it had a single drum spanning almost the full width of the tractor frame. To still further enhance its grip on the ground, its revolving wheel drum could be filled with water-ballast. The Gray had a four-cylinder, crossmounted engine and was advertised with a 20-40 horsepower rating.

Nothing at the Brandon Tractor Demonstration of 1917 was more conspicuous than the Ford car converted to a plowing unit by means of the Tractford attachment, which brought low drive wheels to the rear, replacing the usual tire wheels. With the operator sitting comfortably on a car cushion and enjoying the shade of the touring car's "convertible" top, he presented a picture of easy farming and easy living. It did not escape the notice of spectators that a farmer with such an outfit could plow right up to the customary quitting time on Saturday night, then change to standard car wheels and drive to town for the week's groceries. That Tractford attachment could be bought for $185, f.o.b. Regina, about the price of an average farm horse. But nobody was sure how long an automobile's gears and other mechanisms designed for a totally different form of work would last under the grueling load of plows.

With the multiplicity of designs came a new and more vigorous brand of salesmanship. Manufacturers and dealers knew they would have to be aggressive if they were to secure even a modest share of the market. In their desire to be convincing, salesmen exaggerated in an unconscionable manner and some of them in later years distinguished themselves in the best Liars' Clubs. Farmers who remembered the salesmen of steam tractor days realized that men of the new breed made the old ones seem like beginners. Supported by company advertising, dealers bombarded farming people as never before.

The promoters of the Waterloo Boy—one of the better tractors of the period—were offering free Tractor Schools in 1917. Students received useful instruction about the fundamentals of internal combustion engines and at the same time, a long list of reasons why they should buy a Waterloo Boy.

"Built like a battleship, runs like a watch," was the widely-heralded slogan which helped to sell the British-made Marshall tractor. And for anybody interested in the Made-In-Winnipeg Sterling 12-24 tractor at $1,170, there was the standing offer: "Come to Winnipeg to see it and we will pay the expenses of every purchaser."

For effective advertising, company men trying to sell Happy Farmers at $850, Winnipeg, were most practical: "Sell four horses and buy a Happy Farmer," the invitation read. (*Grain Growers' Guide*, Jan. 24, 1917.) "By selling four horses you could buy a Happy Farmer tractor that would do the work of six or eight. And do it in one-third of the time and at half the expense. Reliable figures show that to feed four horses it takes the crop of 20 acres. By feeding this to steers you could produce 3,600 pounds of beef in a year, bringing big prices. . . . The one-man Happy Farmer tractor does away with the hired help problem. You don't have to look for help when it's scarce nor pay high wages."

This was reasoning farmers understood and they bought Happy Farmers, placing those three-wheel units among the leaders in numbers sold in 1917 and 1918.

As tractor trade gained momentum during those World War I years, the old question of customs duty on farm machinery returned to controversy. Farmers, traditionally freetraders anyway, demanded removal of the duty on small tractors, the 27½ per cent charged on wholesale value at point of purchase in the United States. Nearly all the tractors that farmers were buying, were American-made, and the removal of duty seemed to be the least the government could do if it was serious in its call for more production. It would mean a saving of several hundred dollars on an average tractor. Using J. I. Case tractors as examples, the following shows how the duty affected Canadian farmers.

Size of Tractor	*Factory Price at Racine, Wis.*	*Winnipeg Retail Price*	*Cost of Duty, Exclusive of Freight*
9-18 h.p.	$1,225	$1,610	$325
10-20 h.p.	1,425	1,875	390
12-25 h.p.	2,150	2,835	625

On the tractors sold out of Lethbridge alone in 1917—slightly more than 200 of them—farmers paid more than $60,000 in duty. Of the total number sold, only three of the tractors were made in Canada. But the Government of Canada recognized the inconsistency and an order in council on February 8, 1918, removed the duty on tractors costing $1,400 or less, such concession to last for one year. "His Excellency the Governor-General-In-Council on the recommendation of the Minister of Customs, and under and by virtue of the power in that behalf conferred by the War Measures Act, 1914, or otherwise vested in the Governor-General-In-Council is pleased to order, and it is hereby ordered as follows: During the period of one year from the seventh day of February, 1918, remission, and rebate of duty is hereby authorized in respect to traction engines costing not more than $1,400 in the country of production, designed to be moved by steam or other motive power for farm purposes, and parts thereof for repair, and traction attachments designed and imported. . . ."

As always, the government was taking many words to say what farmers were repeating in two or three, but as anticipated, the removal of duty was an immediate incentive and tractor sales increased. Men who had sneered just a year or so before were inquiring about the new prices. The total number of tractors imported to Canada in the fiscal year ending March 31, 1917, was 2,792—most of them to Western Canada—with a value of $3,259,670. For the next year, ending March 31, 1918, the imports totaled 5,733 tractors, valued at $6,012,343.

By this time another force was at work: Allied Governments were placing orders for tractors in the hope of being ready for the postwar needs and demands to offset food losses due to enemy submarines. Anyway it was viewed, it looked more like a tractor age.

Reynolds Museum Photo

Gray tractor, 18-36 h.p., 1919.

Western Development Museum Photo

The struggling, impoverished farmer had high hopes for the Ford-A-Tractor, a conversion kit which changed his Model T to a vehicle that would draw plows and harrows.

Chapter 21

"The Greater Production Fleet" of 1918

AS THE CRUEL and costly World War I conflict wore on, German submarines extended their range and tightened the blockade aimed at Atlantic shipping. Destruction of ships carrying essential supplies to the United Kingdom and the Allies would bring them to submission, the enemy leaders reasoned. During 1915, Britain lost 885,000 tons of shipping and in 1916, the losses exceeded a million tons. Food as well as munitions was being destroyed at rates no country could stand for very long. Britain and the Allies faced the threat of famine. British farmers were requested to plow up their precious grasslands and grow more wheat, and at the same time, Canadian farmers were urged to increase the production of food commodities by any means possible, concentrating upon those products wanted for export.

The slogan "Food Will Win The War" was sounded with increasing frequency in the early part of 1918. Politicians proclaimed it and farmers, seeking moral reasons for keeping their sons at home when reinforcements were wanted for the armed services, hastened to repeat it. But thousands of young men were entering the army, many of them from farms, and the resulting shortage of manpower certainly compounded the difficulty of raising agricultural output. Bankers, dentists, and real estate agents offered to help farmer friends on Saturday afternoons but their willingness was not enough. Farmers needed full-time workers in substantial numbers to drive their horse outfits or they needed tractor power which would allow more effective use of workers who were available.

The desirability of improving pulling power for farm plows was accepted, but the means of achieving it met with continued argument. The horsemen were not ready to surrender. The breeders continued to argue that heavy horses of good type could be driven in bigger team units to meet the needs of the time. It sounded simple enough; if every teamster doing field work would drive an eight-horse or twelve-horse hitch instead of the traditional four-horse team, a huge saving in farm manpower would be effected. Methods of hitching and driving the multiple units were tested, and pamphlets with diagrams were available to all who might be interested. Normally, a farmer's eight workhorses would be driven as two four-horse teams by two teamsters; why not throw them together to be driven as an eight-horse outfit by one man? When hitched according to recommendations from the Horse and Mule Association of America, such an outfit—or a bigger one consisting of twelve or sixteen horses—could be handled with four reins, very much as a simple four-horse team would be driven.

While the traditionalists were searching for reasons why the new tractor wonders would never replace the time-tested draft horses, Wayne Dinsmore, secretary of the Percheron Horse Society of America, was proclaiming what every loyal horseman wanted to hear: "Farm and city alike will require large numbers of powerful drafters. . . . Armies require horses. Experience has shown they are indispensable. . . . Developments to date indicate that tractors may supplement but not displace heavy draft horses. . . . The fact remains that the horse is a self-repairing, self-reproducing motive power, and the tractor is not. The horse utilizes roughage such as corn fodder, straw and pasturage produced on the farm as a considerable share of his fuel, and all fuel for the tractor must be bought." (*Grain Growers' Guide* May 8, 1918, p. 15.)

Canada's horse population was close to its highest point in all time, and dealers like Alex Galbraith, Edmonton, Vanstone and Rogers, North Battleford, and Colquhoun and Beattie, Brandon, were still importing large numbers of draft stallions and selling them to individual farmers and breeding syndicates across the West.

But in spite of wishful thinking on the part of horse dealers, the reappraisal of farm power was working progressively to the advantage of the small, compact and

The Canadian Government purchased a thousand Fordsons in 1918 and sold them to western farmers at cost, plus freight charges, The first carload of tractors for Saskatchewan arrived at Melfort on May 14, 1918, and created a local stir seldom surpassed.

Henry Ford Museum Photo

versatile gasoline or kerosene tractors. The fact was obvious that tractor efficiency had been changed and improved more rapidly than horse efficiency. The Case Company still offered steam tractors in sizes ranging from 30 to 110 horsepower—all heavyweights, all capable of breaking bridges and getting mired in soft ground, but the low-priced automobile and the low-priced gasoline or kerosene tractor were on the march. Saskatchewan in 1908—the year of the first motor competition at Winnipeg—issued a total of seventy-four automobile licenses, nearly all of which were to city users. But in 1918, car licenses in that province reached 33,000, with a big percentage of them being taken by farmers. Men in a hurry begrudged the time for a horse and buggy trip to town and could not overlook the 1918 chance to buy a new Ford touring car for $495, f.o.b. Ford, Ontario.

It was upon this scene that a radically different, trend-setting small tractor entered with Government of Canada participation. Such government involvement with one particular make of tractor would not have been tolerated in peacetime, but this was wartime and the purpose of making the new tractors available to farmers at cost was to increase the resources of field power in order to raise the production of urgently-needed farm goods. It was simply another wartime measure and was accepted as being quite legitimate.

The price of the new tractor was, indeed, attractive, partly because the Government of Canada, working under War Measures legislation, acted to rebate the duty on tractors entering the country for farm use and costing not more than $1,400 in the country of origin. Western farmers, generally freetraders in their convictions, had been pleading for a permanent cancellation of duty rather than a temporary rebate, but they were thankful for even a one-year concession and increased their purchases accordingly, as figures included in the previous chapter indicate.

Even more significant than the price was the impact of this small tractor with a road speed of eight miles an hour and a unit frame construction. It was a Ford product, to carry the name "Fordson," and it was to influence tractor design throughout the western world. Henry Ford, in 1915, announced his intention of manufacturing a small tractor in sufficient numbers to allow the price to be around $300. It was in line with an earlier declaration on the part of the noted American manufacturer to offer a tractor, a truck, and a car which a farmer could purchase for a total of $1,000. It was a purpose he came very close to achieving.

Manufacture of the Fordson began in 1917 and there was an immediate order from the British Government for 6,000 tractors. The new tractors appeared early in 1918 when the farm power situation was at its most critical point. And following the British example, the Canadian Government ordered Fordsons. A news report from Ottawa, February 12, 1918, announced what the Federal Government chose to call the Canadian Greater Production Fleet. "The Government has purchased a thousand Ford tractors at cost," the report told. (*Grain Growers' Guide,* Feb. 20, 1918, p. 52.) "They will be sold to Canadian farmers also at cost plus freight. Details of freight costs have not yet been worked out but it is estimated that the average cost to the farmer, including freight, will be about $800. In addition, the government has secured options on another thousand tractors.

"The Ford tractor has not so far been supplied to any private individuals. The Ford factories are now engaged on an order for some thousands of the new tractors for the British Government. When the order is completed—probably by the end of March—delivery in Canada will begin. Purchases were completed for Canada after tests made of the tractor by Hon. C. A. Dunning of Regina, and J. D. McGregor, Winnipeg, representing the Minister of Agriculture. Both Mr. Dunning and Mr. McGregor express themselves as fully satisfied with the work of the tractor and are convinced of its practicability. The tractor burns either kerosene or gasoline. A fuel consumption of 2½ gallons of kerosene per acre is regarded as a fair average. It is claimed for the tractor that it can plow an average of eight acres in 10 hours. The plowing speed is given as 2¾ miles per hour. Condition of sale will be cash only. The scheme of distribution remains to be worked out in detail. In all probability, however, orders will be placed through provincial Departments of Agriculture."

A month later it was announced that the Fordson would be sold for $795 cash, delivered at any point in Western Canada, and that orders could be placed with provincial departments of agriculture. The fact of federal and provincial governmental involvement seemed to bring prestige and farmers were eager to purchase. Deliveries to western farmers began in May. The first carload to Saskatchewan's Carrot River Valley arrived at Melfort on May 14 and created a local stir seldom surpassed. One of the tractors in that initial delivery was taken by the MacEwans, of Melfort, and for the balance of the season its engine was rarely allowed to become cool.

When tractors of many kinds were assembled for the 1918 plowing demonstrations at Brandon, a representative of the Greater Production Fleet was there among them, making an impressive showing. Of forty-four tractor entries the Fordson was one of the smallest but it received a disproportionate share of public attention, giving support for the observation that if big tractors were for big farms, small tractors should be for small farms and there were more small farms than big ones.

Again the collection of tractors at Brandon was big and varied and confusing. Only the plows they pulled were similar in shape and design, and for the first time, all had automatic lifts, making it possible for each plowing outfit to be handled by one man. The Fordson, pulling two plows, handling easily, traveling briskly, and exposing no moving parts except its unprotected wheels, looked like the Spirit of 1918.

Before the end of the year, 1,132 Fordson tractors had been brought into Canada and most of them were delivered in the midwestern provinces. Some thousands of acres were added to the cultivated totals and although the war had ended, farm needs had not changed perceptibly. And more significant than the extra acres brought into cultivation as a result of the Greater Production Fleet were the new ideas about the place of small tractors on western farms.

Following Ford's entry into tractor manufacture, certain other automobile companies acted similarly. The company turning out Overland cars acquired the Moline plant, and General Motors, about the same time, took over the Samson. One result was new competition; another was a tendency to higher speed in motors. Farmers took comfort in the thought that well-known automobile manufacturers could not afford to turn out anything except reliable tractors.

Chapter 22

Farm Voices on Costs

FARMERS LEAVING their summerfallowing and other midseason duties long enough to attend the annual contests and demonstrations at Winnipeg and Brandon saw and marveled at new power machines and noted the outward differences in construction, but they came away no wiser about the comparative costs of plowing with horses, steam tractors, and gasoline tractors. It was all very well to talk about horsepower and convenience, but men obliged to borrow the money with which to make major purchases wanted to know that a tractor would be more than a luxury. The essential information on operational costs was still hopelessly inadequate. Tractor salesmen, seeing no sin in trying to give their machines the appearance of perfection, told fantastic stories bearing no relationship to facts.

Farmers were mystified, and universities and experimental farms were of little or no help. That they had a responsibility in answering questions about the economics of farm power, and should have been conducting comprehensive cost studies with horses and the various types of mechanical power, continued to elude the notice of public workers. The farmer's question was a simple one: "When all things, including interest on investment and depreciation, are considered, can a steam or gasoline tractor plow more cheaply than my horses?" Many farmers attending the exhibition performances admitted fascination, but failing to find the information they considered essential, simply renewed their former prejudices in favor of horses or steam or gasoline as the case might be.

If the professors of agriculture did not have the needed information and the machine companies were not likely to support co-operative testing, the remaining hope was in drawing upon farm experience, scarce and limited though it might be. "Let's hear from farmers who have conducted their own tests," an editor wrote pleadingly. Fortunately, a few farm operators were in a position to report on side-by-side tests with horses and either or both of the types of tractors commanding attention.

Of those farmers reporting prior to the end of World War I, while heavy tractors were still in the majority, most of them showed their horses well ahead in efficiency. One of the exceptions, whose report was publicized in Western Canada, was J. A. Kyle, of Kansas. Having placed his 30-horsepower gasoline tractor costing $3,000 against 30 work-horses valued at $150 each, he proceeded to break a large area of prairie land and record the costs, including labor, and board for the laborers. Perhaps his humane feeling for animals weakened his objectivity in conducting experimental work. Anyway, the breaking of new land, he noted, was a task too severe for horses, and his figures showed his gasoline tractor delivering the cheaper power for the purpose. The tractor, in addition to having the lower overhead cost, was able to do the same amount of breaking as the horses were doing but with a saving in operational costs of $18.30 per day. (*Farm and Ranch Review*, May 5, 1911, p. 285.)

On the other hand, Wayne Dinsmore, the unfailing champion of heavy horses, presented Canadian figures which made the tractor seem like a poor choice for plowing purposes. (*Grain Growers' Guide*, Oct. 28, 1914, p. 27.) Dinsmore's most conclusive evidence came from Alberta farmer Charles Esterbrook who could relate cost figures for both a 45-horsepower gasoline tractor and draft horses working the same land. The Esterbrook costs with both tractor and horses were worked out on a per-day basis—313 working days per year—as follows:

Tractor Costs	*Cost per day*
Interest at 7% on $3,990, being the purchase price of tractor and plow	.88
Depreciation at 25% of $3,990	3.19
Gasoline, 45 gallons at 33⅓ cents per gallon delivered at farm	15.00
Cylinder oil, 3 gallons at 80 cents per gallon	2.40
Gear oil, 1 gallon at 30 cents per gallon	.30
Hard oil and transmission grease	.10
Engineer's wage	5.00
Plowman's wage	3.50
Board for engineer and plowman at 50 cents per day	1.00
Total per day	31.37

Plowing an average of 20 acres per day, the cost was $1.57 per acre.
Horse Costs

Interest at 7% on investment of $450 in each six horse plowing unit	.10
Depreciation on horses nil because increasing value of young horses counterbalances decreasing value of older ones,	nil
Depreciation of 10% on gang plow and repairs at 5%	.04
Interest on $90 investment in gang plow	.02
Driver's wages at $40 per month	1.53
Board for driver	.50
Feed for six horses (each receiving 4½ gallons of oats worth 32 cents per bushel and 21 pounds of hay worth $7 per ton)	1.65
Interest on harness worth $120	.0268
Depreciation on harness at 10% and repairs at 5%	.057
Sharpening plow points at 30 cents per day	.30
Total per day	4.22

Plowing five acres per day, the cost with horses was 84 cents per acre, very much lower than the figure of $1.57 per acre for plowing with the Esterbrook tractor.

"Look out for those hidden costs," Dinsmore seemed to be saying to prairie farmers. If it was not for the high price of horses, the dealer's willingness to sell for a small cash payment, and the purchaser's ignorance about high depreciation and interest costs, there would be scarcely any sales of tractors. Concluding observations about his tour of Western Canada, Dinsmore said that "at numerous places tractors were found idle in the farmyards or sheds while farmers were doing the field work with horses." But while the great spokesman for the horse interests was making his report, tractor dealers were making more and more sales and some were accusing him of the same sort of biased salesmanship which had made tractor agents a menace in farming communities.

It was almost impossible to find anyone who could and would speak without bias on the subject of farm power. If he was a manufacturer or dealer in tractors, he had something to sell; if he was a breeder of draft horses, he was likely to possess sentiments of loyalty rivaling those of a Scotsman for Scotland or an Irishman for Ireland. Consequently, the controversy continued for years. During that period, the favorite topics in country schoolhouse debates were: "*Resolved,* That farming is preferable to city living," and "*Resolved,* That horses will furnish better and cheaper farm power than either steam or gasoline tractors."

Those who upheld the side of horses in those memorable country debates preceding the years of more sophisticated entertainment never failed to draw upon the precise experience reported from the celebrated Noble Farms in southern Alberta. The conclusions, based upon the extensive operation of all three types of field power, were difficult to refute and they attracted more public attention and influenced more farming people than anything published at the time. They also made a strong case for horses, even on big farms of the plains where mechanical power should have found its best working conditions. The tractors involved, of course, were mainly those of the heavy type.

Charles Sherwood Noble was a man of stature and anybody knowing him would recognize honest purpose in his widely-heralded conclusions about power costs. Born in Iowa in 1873, Mr. Noble came to Alberta in 1902 and homesteaded in the Claresholm district. Seven years later he bought 5,000 acres of prairie land northwest of Lethbridge and embarked upon large-scale farming which attracted the attention of the agricultural world. In 1913, a company under the name of Noble Foundation was formed and expansion continued until operations reached a maximum of 33,000 acres under cultivation. There were reverses as unmistakable as bankruptcy, but there were recoveries and triumphs in the form of world records in grain production. In 1915, the farm produced 126 bushels of oats per acre from 1,075 acres, and in the next year the average yield from 1,000 acres of Marquis wheat was 54.23 bushels per acre.

The most widely-discussed figures from the Noble Foundation cost records were based on double discing and harrowing of new breaking, and the nub of the report was that gasoline tractors did the work at 70 cents per acre, steam tractors at 60 cents and horses at 42 cents per acre. But because the Noble experience with power was quoted so often, it is appropriate to let Charles Noble—later Dr. Charles Noble—relate the circumstances in his own words (*Grain Growers' Guide,* June 16, 1920, p. 1380):

"In breaking prairie we have used steamers extensively and we believe with profit, since we pull heavy rollers behind the plows pressing down the newly turned sod more effectively than could be done with ordinary packers. The horses we employ to follow immediately behind the plows to work a light mulch on the rolled breaking with discs and harrows. The quality of the breaking is fully equal to that done by horses.

"In plowing summerfallow we have also used steamers extensively but in this kind of plowing horses do much better work. The land is kept more nearly level and a more uniform seed bed can be prepared. At the present prices on grain we believe that horse-plowed land will produce from three to four dollars worth more grain per acre than that plowed with steamers. The delays due to rain are much less frequent with horses than with engines in summerfallowing work, and our only reason for using them is that we have not yet been able to get our horse power up to the point where all the work can be done in the proper season.

"We find no economy in man power in using a steamer as compared with the horses, as three men, each with ten horses strung out in pairs on a three bottom plow, will make quite as good an average for a season's summerfallow plowing as a 32 h.p. steam engine, which requires four or five men to operate.

"Regarding gas tractors, until 1918 we used only three or four different engines but during 1918 and 1919 we used a number of 12-24 engines at various kinds of work. We have always made it a point with our gas engines to employ the best men obtainable to operate them, but even then we have not found them as satisfactory as horses. Delays on account of weather are frequent and repair bills, no matter how good the attention, are always high and the cost of fuel and oil is not only high but is becoming higher month by month.

"In 1918 we had a good opportunity to compare horses, steamers and gas tractors in working down with discs and

Wartime demands for food led to some large-scale operations, such as this harvest scene at Snipe Lake, Saskatchewan, in 1915, on the Gartside farm.

harrows, several thousand acres of newly broken and rolled land. The gas tractors were of 12 tractive h.p. and each one pulled three eight-foot discs with harrows behind. The same load was hauled by eight horses driven abreast. Four similar outfits were handled by each 32 h.p. steam engine. The conditions of weather and soil were unusually favorable and were uniform for several months for the various kinds of power employed. The costs for double discing and harrowing were as follows: horses, 42 cents per acre; steamers, 60 cents per acre, and gas tractors, 70 cents per acre. In figuring these costs no depreciation was charged. With this included the showing would have been much more in favor of the horses as with them the depreciation is very low indeed, whereas with tractors it is considerable. The conditions of land and weather during the trial were more nearly perfect for tractors than one can reasonably hope for ordinarily, so that we do not believe we are overstating it when we say that under average conditions the showing made by tractors in the above trial is as good, if not better, than we might expect for most farm operations.

"In our experience, no matter how large or small the farm, it requires no more horses to do the plowing, discing and other cultural operations in good season than to seed, harvest and market a crop. These latter operations, most farmers will agree, can best be done with horses.

"For our freighting we depend largely on horses, but during 1918 and 1919 we did a great deal of heavy hauling with two 3½-ton trucks, each truck hauling from four to five tons. Most of the haul was over a graded earth road from 20 to 30 miles. On account of the dry seasons the roads were unusually good and few delays were encountered. During the same period we did a great deal of freighting with 12-horse teams strung out in pairs, using three or four wagons loaded with from 15 to 20 tons. With the best of care and attention, the trucks required no small amount of repairing and the depreciation was very heavy; with the horse outfit there was much less grief and lower bills for both depreciation and repair. We have been forced to conclude that, even under these conditions, which look favorable for trucks, our freighting can be done more economically with horses, and we have abandoned the trucks, except possibly a light one for errand work.

"At present we are feeding our horses oats worth $1.15 per bushel and allowing gas tractors and trucks to stand idle. Under our conditions, we believe this is good business. We are, however, quite prepared to admit that under certain conditions gas tractors can be profitably used. We have found it no small advantage at times to have a few tractors available to carry us over a rush of work, but with the initial cost so high and fuel very expensive, with often inadequate service from jobbers, that we cannot afford to depend on them with profit. We believe that where they can be operated by a mechanically inclined owner better service can be had than where dependence is placed on hired mechanics.

"We believe that no matter how reasonable engines, parts and fuel may be, it would be a great mistake to neglect the breeding and working of the best type of farm horses."

The words were those of the Master of Noble Foundation, a Western Figure with whom nobody argued very loudly. They were words with which most farming people in 1919 and 1920 were ready to agree. The statement did not terminate the arguments but it won widespread attention and rated as a classic in the history of farm power.

Chapter 23

The Postwar Years

FROM THE ADVERSITY OF WAR, farmers learned some lessons, among them that a worker's output is determined by the power and machinery he commands. A man with two horses and a fourteen-inch walking plow turned less than two acres per day, just as such a worker had been doing since the early years of agriculture. Considering the amount of ground cultivated, efficiency in the use of horses had not changed in a generation. Acres cultivated per horse in Canada and the United States were about the same in 1920 as in 1900. But tractors, in the course of the same period, changed greatly, making it possible for farm operators to double or triple the output per worker.

Horse population was at its highest point in 1920 and 1921—26,000,000 horses and mules in the United States and 3,610,494 in Canada—and nearly one-quarter of the cultivated acreage was being used to grow feed. Tractor sales, which had grown during the war years, continued to rise after the period of urgency in food production should have passed, and even more spectacular was the growth in automobile sales, with farmers as the principal buyers.

When the Winnipeg Exhibition of 1910 conducted the first automobile trial to complement the famous Winnipeg motor contests, a motorized road vehicle was still a novelty, especially on country trails where thoughtful drivers could not escape a fear of being stranded far from a blacksmith shop and source of repairs. The idea of being towed back to town by a team of farm horses suggested humiliation no automobile owner cared to contemplate. On that Winnipeg Exhibition occasion, each automobile contestant was given a can containing half a gallon of gasoline and was required to travel at not less than 15 miles per hour until the fuel was exhausted. The object was to see how far each car could go, and the winner was the Brush machine which traveled 18½ miles and had a pint of gasoline left in its tank. The performance was rated at about 48 miles per gallon, which would seem remarkable enough even 50 years later. A Ford entry went 17 miles and 704 yards before running out of gas; the Maytag did 17 miles and 352 yards; the Hupmobile was next with a distance of 16 miles and 1,232 yards, then the Franklin with 13 miles and 1,408 yards and the Reo with 9 miles and 1,232 yards. In the second part of the test, the hill climb, it was again the Brush automobile which gained the highest score while the Maytag was second.

Farmers attending the Winnipeg Exhibition of 1910 watched the lumbering tractors with keen interest but saw the automobiles as instruments of amusement rather than utility. The idea of abandoning their horse-drawn buggies, democrats, and wagons seemed totally remote and impractical. Anybody who owned a team of good road horses knew he had no reason to complain, and young farmers were still satisfied to conduct the ancient game of courting behind a dashboard and a slow horse. But seven years later, according to one writer (Higginbotham, H., "Automobiles in Western Canada," *Grain Growers' Guide,* Nov. 7, 1917, p. 27), "the increase in the number of automobiles among farmers is nothing short of phenomenal. The driving horse is passing rapidly with the farmer as it has already passed with the city professional and business man."

The Brandon Exhibition of 1917 furnished proof when an estimated 5,000 autos were said to be parked on the grounds at one time. Saskatoon saw an Automobile Day being celebrated in conjunction with the exhibition there. A prize of $100 was offered for the town or community represented with the largest number of motor vehicles on the exhibition grounds, and the district of Allan, east of Saskatoon, was declared the winner, having sent forty-five automobiles to the fair. Langham was second with forty-three automobiles.

The 1917 increase in the number of automobiles in Saskatchewan was so rapid that the provincial license department could not cope with the flow of applications, and when the supply of metal license plates became exhausted, the officials at Regina were obliged to fall back upon printed tags to be pasted on windshields. Reporting for the year,

Hupp Yeats Electric, 1911 (top).

Hupmobile (center).

Franklin, 1911 (bottom).

the deputy provincial secretary could tell of issuing 32,505 car licenses, double the number registered in the province in the previous year. In a province of about 650,000 people, the automobile licenses of 1917 represented one motor vehicle for every twenty persons, a ratio which made writers conclude that Saskatchewan was leading the world in cars per capita. For all of Canada, the 1917 ratio was one car for every fifty-seven of human population, a record of car ownership said to be exceeded by only two countries in the world.

Alberta, by 1917, had 20,623 cars, with most of them owned by farming people; Manitoba had 17,507, and British Columbia, 11,625. The total of 82,260 cars owned in Western Canada in that year represented a much bigger acceptance of motor travel than was the case in the East. And sales continued to rise; the western total of 165,197 registered automobiles in 1920 represented more than twice the car population of 1917, and the Canadian car industry, with capital investment of $50,000,000 and plants at Chatham, Oshawa, Ford City, London, Walkerville, and Toronto, was preparing for bigger things. The manufacturers' faith was amply rewarded because Canadians, by 1928, were the owners of one car for every twelve of human population and Westerners had one car for every eight people.

Reynolds Museum Photo

L. R. McLeod Photo

Reynolds Museum Photo

International Harvester Titan, 10-20 horsepower, 1917 (top).

International Harvester Mogul, 10-20 horsepower, 1917 (center).

Waterloo Boy gas tractor, 1918 (bottom).

Western tractor sales did not experience quite the same bullish spurt as car sales, but the rate of increase was remarkably steady. Sales for the three midwestern provinces totaled 5,000 in 1917 and increased to more than double that number—10,279—in 1920.

Contrary to expectations, the call for increased food production which Canadian farmers heard so clearly throughout the period of war, did not cease at war's end. Many parts of the world came to the time of Armistice with empty larders, and Canadian farmers knew exactly what was expected of them. Horse numbers had not increased fast enough to meet all needs, and instead of terminating their interest in mechanical power as the sceptics had predicted, farmers continued to purchase tractors.

But tractor production in 1920 was still in turmoil. New makes with new names and shapes as varied as human figures were appearing with almost every issue of the farm magazines; and almost as frequently, tractors with only faintly familiar names were disappearing. Still others were becoming better known and adding to records of reliability. The Hart-Parr tractors deserved the honor accorded pioneers in the field. The International Harvester Company was offering tractors in various sizes and reporting phenomenal sales of the Titan 10-20, so great that it was necessary to warn prospective customers of a delay of several months in making deliveries on these popular two-cylinder, three-plow tractors. J. I. Case Co. was advertising a line of gasoline-burning and kerosene-burning tractors but still offering steam tractors in eight sizes. Only 104 steamer tractors were sold in the entire West in 1919 and 89 in 1920. Most of them, no doubt, carried the familiar Case trademark depicting a bald eagle perched on top of a globe. It seemed to be sentiment more than the quest for profit that held the big steamers in the company catalogues so long.

A western farmer desiring to buy a gasoline or kerosene tractor in 1920 or 1921 could count at least fifty types and sizes from which to make a choice. The long list included the Waterloo Boy being offered by the John Deere Plow Co., the familiar Fordson, Avery, Sawyer-Massey, Massey-Harris, Emerson-Brantingham, Advance Rumely, Happy Farmer, Wallis, Aultman-Taylor, Gray, Heider, Stinson, Turner, Twin City, Lacrosse, Beaver, George White, Eagle Lauson, Plowman, G-O, Allwork, and others. There were several tractors on tracks instead of wheels, the Holt Caterpillar, Monarch Neverslip, Cletrac and Bates Steel Mule, the latter with tracks behind and conventional wheels in front. Several attachments for converting Ford cars to two-plow tractor units were still on the market, one of them being the Ford-A-Tractor, guaranteed to do a four-horse job in the fields and being offered for $200.

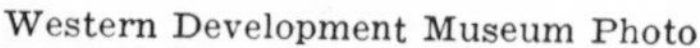

Western Development Museum Photo

Western Development Museum Photo

Western Development Museum Photo

Happy Farmer Lacrosse tractor, 1915 (top left).

Monarch Neverslip, 1916 (top right).

Holt gasoline crawler, 1908.

Reynolds Museum Photo

Reynolds Museum Photo

Powell Equipment Photo

Canadian Tractor, made in Medicine Hat around 1916. This was the only tractor built in Alberta and was unique by virtue of its wooden spokes and wooden beam.

Alberta Museum and Archives Photo

Most of the many tractors displayed on the advertising pages of the farm papers were of United States' make. There were a few exceptions like the Chase, manufactured by the Chase Tractor Corporation, Toronto, and the Canadian, made at Medicine Hat.

The Canadian was a 14-28 horsepower tractor and the announcement of 1920 telling of its production in Alberta was greeted with hopeful interest. The West wanted industry, and there was rejoicing that Medicine Hat and the supplies of cheap natural gas had attracted one in which agricultural people would be interested. The Alberta Foundry and Machine Co. had been engaged in manufacturing munitions during the war years, and when hostilities ceased, the Medicine Hat plant was retooled to make tractors.

The Alberta-made tractor had its distinctive features. Instead of being an all-metal machine, it was of metal and wood construction. A squared hardwood beam running longitudinally constituted the basic part of the framework and squared wood of the same kind provided the spokes in the drive wheels. The beam was squared to 9 inches by 9 inches and each of the 16 spokes—8 in each drive wheel—was 3⅛ inches by 3⅛ inches in cross-section.

The Canadian Tractor was supposed to have been thoroughly tested in 1919 and its performance was said to justify large-scale production. Early in 1920, the company was ready for business and invited farmers to investigate "The wonderful $1200 tractor with fewer parts than in a binder." One of the earliest announcements told that the tractor was already in such demand that delivery could not be guaranteed for four months after orders were placed. It sounded well but the optimism was never justified. The dry prairie climate was said to have caused shrinking of the wood in construction, and this coupled with certain mechanical flaws and poor crops in the Medicine Hat area led to failure. About forty of the Canadians were manufactured and sold, one of which survives as the property of the Reynolds Museum at Wetaskiwin and on loan to the Provincial Museum at Edmonton.

It was the fate of various tractors designed in haste and placed on the market before being adequately tested.

The advance of mechanization was always marked by irregular steps, some backward as well as forward. As the West felt the impact of postwar depression, tractor sales fell away. Not until recovery in 1926 did they resume their spectacular rise. In the intervening years, horse breeders found restored confidence, talking as though they had routed the evil engines forever. "Right must triumph over evil," one was heard to say quite righteously. Horses were of God's creating; man, with the help of the Devil, made the tractors.

Chapter 24

Horsemen Hear Call to Rally

NEITHER the Charles S. Noble reports favoring horses for field work nor the decline in tractor sales during a brief postwar recession brought more than fleeting comfort to the breeders of Clydesdales, Percherons, and Belgians. The specialized horsemen were worried more than ever before. Outwardly, their business operations appeared very much as usual. Their fat and heavy stallions being "traveled" by devoted grooms from one "stand" to another in rural communities were still familiar sights. Hitched to two-wheeled carts or led behind pony-drawn vehicles, the big studs moved with much whinnying to advertise themselves from farm to farm, leaving undetermined numbers of mares to become mothers about eleven months hence. But farmers were becoming indifferent about breeding mares and stallion enrollment was dropping ominously from its highest point in 1918.

Members of the horse breeders' associations were cautioned to work harder in the promotion of their business, and governments were asked for increased financial encouragement in the form of subsidies to be applied to service fees for approved stallions. Importers, dealers, and breeders of purebred stock responded dutifully. Treating the new mechanical power with fine scorn, they advertised their adopted breeds and exhibited their best animals very much as they had been doing for years. Horse classes at western fairs and exhibitions were as big and impressive and controversial as ever.

At the Brandon Winter Fair in March, 1920, for example, no fewer than twenty-eight aged Clydesdale stallions—every one a potential champion in the eyes of his owner—lined up in a single class to face Judge William Gibson, of Indian Head. It may have been the last time such an aggregation of breeding power appeared in one ring. Selected to win that magnificent class of sires was Ben Finlayson's imported Dunure Gayman, a massive horse displaying some conscious pride in being the son of the celebrated Baron of Buchlyvie. In another ring, a class of sixteen Percheron stallions lined up for judging and the big black Marquisat, owned by Trotter and Trotter, Brandon, was chosen to win. At other winter fairs across the West, the stallion classes were correspondingly big and there was no outward evidence of retreat on the part of the horse exhibitors.

Supporters of the heavy breeds gave the usual rapt attention when men like Prof. W. L. Carlyle, manager of the Bar U Ranch, made speeches proclaiming the imperishable qualities of draft horses and tried to be helpful. Addressing the Alberta Horse Breeders' Association in 1920 (*Agricultural Alberta, Edmonton,* Vol. 1, No. 1, July, 1920), he noted how wartime circumstances forced many farmers, hard pressed to obtain the needed labor, to buy tractors for which they had but scant enthusiasm. Now, there would be reassessment of costs, and in the light of experience on the Bar U Ranch, farmers would find tractor plowing to be costing fully one-third more than plowing when they used the old reliable horses. "The horse," said he, "is going to be the mainstay on our farms while the tractor will be used as an adjunct to the horse for stationary engine purposes and to take off the peak load during the busy seasons. . . . Any man with a good draft mare is foolish if he does not breed her to a good draft stallion . . . the man with a poor draft mare is equally foolish if he breeds her at all."

But the need of the hour was for something more than propaganda and fine speeches about faithful work animals. Men on the land were asking the most pertinent questions about the economics of farm power. The Horse Association of America, through its officers, was telling one story which showed horses ahead of motive power in economical performance while the Power Farming Bureau was proclaiming the huge economies in tractor power. When the secretary of the Horse Association of America returned from an inspection of conditions in Manitoba, Saskatchewan, and Alberta in 1921, he expressed the view that most tractors were not being used and 80 per cent of Alberta farmers owning tractors regretted their investment.

At once, the tractor interests conducted a survey among 5,000 tractor owners in Western Canada and obtained information that showed 85 per cent had indeed used their tractors in that year. How was Mr. Farmer to know what to believe?

Even after the tractor gained in popularity and was accepted by the majority of farmers, horsemen were still arguing about the merits of their favorite breeds. Pulling contests for horses were staged, and proved that good teams could indeed move amazing loads.

Three Rivers Commercial photo

W. F. Handschin, professor of farm management at the University of Illinois (*Grain Growers' Guide*, Sept. 3, 1919), had some advice of a kind men of the soil could readily understand. Farmers, he pointed out, could not do much about fixed charges. If they were to reduce costs in production, they had to look mainly to labor and power expenses. His studies over a period of seven years showed horse farmers as having the best opportunity to reduce expenses. Where could they make economies? The farm management specialist offered a six-point proposal:

1—Organize farm work to obtain the maximum yearly use of horses, there being too many working only 600 hours per year instead of a possible 3,000 hours.

2—Adopt more economy in feeding.

3—Use brood mares in the working program.

4—Sell more horses to city buyers before they begin to wear out on the farms.

5—Improve draft horse type.

6—Drive bigger team units.

But even this scholarly fellow may have fallen under the spell of sentiment, as his words suggest: "It has always been my opinion that the tractor never would be a permanent fixture in our farming unless so designed as to wear practically as many years as a horse. . . . It is apparent, therefore, that on the basis of present information the horse is not due to be displaced in any large proportion from farms of the country. I believe he will continue to be, what he always has been, the standard farm power."

Horsemen, wondering what they could and should do to further safeguard their interests, chose to believe that Professor Handschin's fifth point was the most practical. With more horses of approved type and quality, draft efficiency would be improved sufficiently to tip the balance of popularity in their direction. This was their plea when they approached the Federal and Provincial Governments for more assistance. Public officials, traditionally sympathetic to the big and influential fraternity of horsemen, were readily convinced that government policy which had long contributed part of the service fees for approved stallions, should do more. If type improvement could save the horse industry from destruction by tractors, departments of agriculture should be giving leadership. Only by the introduction of sires of genuinely outstanding excellence could the improvement be enough to match or outmatch the tractors in the field of efficiency. It was a lovely hope. It was also fanciful reasoning, but it led to the importation of some truly high-class and high-priced stallions whose names in prairie communities became about as well known as those of leading politicians of the day.

Saskatchewan farmers approved when the Provincial Government, acting upon a request from the Saskatchewan Horse Breeders' Association, decided to purchase one or two of the best Clydesdale stallions obtainable in the home of the breed. A purchasing committee was appointed and, furnished with funds, instructed to sail for Scotland, there to locate and buy one or more of those sires capable of halting the advance of tractors in the prairie wheat fields. Finding the stallion or stallions was not difficult but purchasing proved extremely difficult. The reluctance of Scottish breeders to part with their best breeding animals forced the members of the Saskatchewan committee to consider promising young horses as alternatives to proven sires.

After carefully considering their instructions, they bought Craigie Enchanter and Bonnie Fyvie, both yearlings in 1920. But there was misfortune ahead. Craigie Enchanter died from strangulation due to an intestinal tumor soon after being delivered at Saskatoon and Bonnie Fyvie developed stringhalt and was destroyed in 1926. The ambitious plans brought nothing but disappointment although there was partial compensation for losses sustained when a third stallion, Craigie Fyvie, known as the "Gift Horse"—a full brother of Craigie Enchanter, was sent from Scotland to the University of Saskatchewan.

The Legislature of Alberta, with exactly the same desire to effect improvement in that particular form of field power which farmers were capable of raising, made an appropriation for the purchase of two stallions, the best to be found, one a Clydesdale and the other a Percheron. Craigie Masterpiece, a seven-year-old weighing 2,100 pounds and tested as a breeder and show horse, was bought in Scotland at a cost of about $10,000. Soon thereafter, Job, a big Percheron, was bought in the United States. The latter, foaled in France and used and shown in the United States, cost the government about $8,000. Both stallions were accorded royal welcomes when delivered in Alberta in 1920, and Hon. Duncan Marshall, Minister of Agriculture, pronounced them the best horses ever imported to Canada.

The decision to buy outstanding stallions was a fine gesture and proved government loyalty to horses and horse breeders, but any impact upon the faltering industry was negligible and the money might as well have been spent to provide free merry-go-round rides at the summer fairs. A mere two or three decades later and it would have been extremely difficult to find a purebred Percheron with the name of Job in its pedigree or a Clydesdale with Craigie Masterpiece or Bonnie Fyvie among its ancestors. Horsemen began to realize that something more was needed if draft horses were to retain their long-standing place of preferment on western farms.

All the while, new makes and models of tractors were appearing to haunt the horsemen. They came with a frequency rivaling changes in April weather. Tractors of fifty different kinds were being offered in Western Canada in 1921 and tractor dealers were prospering even more than the importers and dealers in stallions. Spokesmen for the horse interests wanted to do something dramatic—like declare open war upon the terrible engines—and called for suggestions. The Horse Association of America, through its dynamic director, Wayne Dinsmore, succeeded in popularizing big hitches and promoting horse-pulling contests. The pulling events were essentially exhibition stunts but the big hitches, with their roots in the good soil of utility, came close to achieving the desired purpose.

Horsemen had been staging private pulling contests for years. As everybody who ever worked around a threshing outfit knew, it required a powerful and well-trained team—also the steadying influence of an experienced driver—to haul a hundred-bushel load of wheat across a stubble field. The owner of such a team could not hide his pride. Why not make pulling a competitive event, thereby giving draft horses and their owners some of the publicity normally kept for baseball players and engineers working steam tractors on exhibition ramps? A few fairs conducted local contests, using stoneboats piled high with sacks of sand or two-bushel bags of wheat; but to make the competitions uniform, some standardized equipment was needed.

The desired order was brought to the contests when a worker at Iowa State College invented a machine for measuring the exact pulling power of a team. It was a big and cumbersome thing, a dynamometer, but it was capable of removing the guesswork in deciding contest winners and restraining the exaggeration and the prevarication in which horsemen were known to indulge. Saskatchewan's Prof. E. A. Hardy visited Iowa, saw the dynamometer, and returned to make one and have it ready for the fairs and exhibitions of 1924. Shipped from one contest to another, the machine became a center of attraction, and competing under uniform rules, Western Canadian horses began to make records.

The best record up to that time was a pull of 2,500 pounds on the dynamometer for the required distance of 27½ feet. But at Calgary, a team of Clydesdales pulled 2,615 pounds, for which a world record was claimed. With western enthusiasm running high, that record did not stand for long. It was a fast-moving drama and the climax came during the weeks of the Saskatoon and Regina exhibitions. Visitors at the Saskatoon show saw the Bob McLeod team of Percherons pull 2,900 pounds for the qualifying distance to establish an impressive world record. Nor was that the end. At Regina, in the following exhibition week, a massive team of Belgians, Jumbo and Barney, owned by Gibbs Brothers of Lumsden, pulled 3,100 to set a new world record, the third to be made by Canadian horses in less than four weeks.

Dan Elderkin, manager of the Regina Exhibition, sensed opportunity in bringing the Saskatoon and Regina winners together for a special championship match, the battle of the heavyweights. He called his friend and fellow exhibition manager, Sid Johns, of Saskatoon, saying: "I've got a thousand dollars for the winners if you can get Bob McLeod's Percherons here to pull against the Belgians from Lumsden tomorrow afternoon." The jovial Saskatoon manager said he could arrange it, and when the midnight train left Saskatoon a few hours later, one of its express shipments was a team of Percheron geldings. It was an expensive way to move horses but at such a moment, with

Staunch horsemen were loath to accept the advancing mechanistic age and fought back with larger and larger teams of horses in an attempt to prove that animals were as economical and efficient as tractors. They put up a good fight, but eventually they too were forced to bow to a new way of farming.

Western Producer Photo

the honor and glory of two proud cities at stake, who would worry about costs?

The announcement about a meeting of the two champion teams circulated like a rumor of political scandal and at the appointed hour, Dan Elderkin's grandstand seats were full, just as he had anticipated. And why not? It was to be the testing ground for a world championship match, a contest between the favorites of two jealous Saskatchewan communities and a showdown for two great breeds. Nobody would want to miss it. The Gibbs Belgians pulled first, moving 3,000 pounds for the required 27½ feet. The cheers could have been heard half way to Moose Jaw. Then came the McLeod Percherons and pulled exactly the same weight and distance. The suspense grew greater and the Saskatoon supporters became hilarious. The two great teams were tied and there had to be a repeat pull. Both started with a dynamometer reading of 3,100 pounds but neither took it the full distance. Inasmuch as the McLeod horses pulled it the greater distance, namely 18½ feet, they were declared the winners, but the Gibbs Belgians, because of their success on the previous day, were still the world champions.

"There'll be another year," the Regina horsemen were saying, "and we'll show those Saskatoon ponies how to pull."

The teams were taken to their respective homes to recover and train for the next year, 1925. In the ensuing months, they received the best feed and care and attention. Public interest was maintained, and sure enough, both teams returned for the exhibition competition at Regina. By that time, the Belgians weighed almost a ton each and the Percherons between 1,800 and 1,900 pounds each. Both teams were ready. The Saskatoon horses pulled first, moving 3,200 pounds to set a new world record. But it was not a record to stand for many minutes because the Gibbs horses, coming next, pulled 3,300 pounds for the distance and thus recovered the championship with what was still a new world pulling record. There was no doubt about the winners, but purely for purposes of record, the Belgians pulled again, this time doing 3,350 pounds to establish the third world record to be made in that day.

United States editors noted the succession of Canadian victories and chided their own horsemen with the question: "Are Canadian horses really that much better?" American horsemen read the *Breeders' Gazette* challenge: "Come on horse owners of U.S.A." Iowa horsemen were eager to regain the championship and later in 1925 succeeded with a team pulling 3,400 pounds. And on September 1, 1925, a team of Belgian-Percheron crossbreds, pulling at Iowa State Fair at Des Moines, broke some hickory singletrees and bent some steel replacements but pulled 3,425 pounds and emerged as champions which would be hard to beat.

The pulling contests—brief as the period of their popularity had been—served a useful purpose, but practical horsemen knew they could not save their industry from the advancing tractor power with individual feats of strength. The important wage-saving benefits would come only when farmers adopted bigger hitches, requiring fewer hired hands. If men on the land had been drawn to tractors because of effectiveness in extending the production of each worker, why not demonstrate how the same result could be gained by increasing the number of horses to be hitched and handled by one driver? If a man directing twelve horses could do as much field work as three men driving four-horse teams, the economies should be obvious. And with proper hitching methods, one man could, indeed, handle twelve horses—or sixteen or twenty.

Again the big and progressive Noble Foundation farm at Nobleford, Alberta, was held up as an example. C. S. Noble had declared his faith in horses as sources of field power and then set about to demonstrate how they could yield the highest return in work.

"Because a saving in manpower has been effected by the use of tractors is no proof that an equal or greater saving could not have been effected by using horses differently," said James Murray, farm superintendent at the

T. R. Melville-Ness Photos

Noble Foundation farm. (*Grain Growers' Guide,* March 3, 1920.) He proceeded to explain how it could be done. A 12-horse team pulling three seed drills could plant seventy-five acres a day and an 8-horse, 10-horse or 12-horse outfit —depending on the character of the soil—pulling a three-furrow gang plow could turn eight acres a day. Even for freighting and hauling water, the Noble policy was to drive 12 horses strung out in 6 pairs. With such a team, one man on the Noble farm was hauling 140 barrels of water per trip.

The secret was in knowing how to hitch the big outfits in order to insure the best working conditions for the horses and the easiest handling for the teamsters. For drilling or discing, there was not much objection to having the horses hitched abreast, but for plowing, the tandem was necessary if horses were to be spared the hardship of walking on freshly-plowed ground and pulling the extra dead weight created by side-draft. It was proven that horses worked easier when they had good footing and direct pulling such as the tandem hitches afforded. When 8, 10, or 12 horses were engaged in plowing, the Noble recommendations emphasized, they should be driven tandem.

The point of importance was that 12 horses driven in 6 tandem pairs were no more difficult to control than 4 horses driven tandem. The lead team only was driven directly by reins in the hands of the teamster, with all other horses being "tied in" and "bucked back" so they could not get out of position or out of control. The "tying in" was effected by fastening a halter shank or tiechain from the bit of the off-horse to the whippletree or tracechain of the near-horse of the team immediately ahead. Similarly, the near-horse of a pair was tied to the whippletree or trace-chain of the off-horse ahead. At the same time, horses were restrained from pulling ahead by means of the buckstraps or buckropes running from the inside of the bits to the tracechains of the neighboring horses. Adjustment of tie-chains and buckropes was most important; only when a team was in the right pulling position could the buckropes, with no slack, be snapped into the correct positions in the tracechains. With proper adjustment, it was possible for the teamster to drive the lead team and see the rest of his horses under a sort of self-control.

And James Murray repeated a sentiment his employer, Mr. Noble, had expressed, that "the best plowing is done with horses." Moreover, when horses were used in large

A number of loyal horsemen insisted that the best plowing was done with horses, and recommended that teams of eight, ten or twelve horses be hitched tandem for peak efficiency. They did not approve of hitching large teams abreast, because it brought an extra hardship for the horses, as they had to walk on freshly-plowed ground and pull the dead weight created by side draft.

Western Producer Photo

units, "they are a cheaper source of power for most farm operations than either gas or steam. On the Noble Foundation Farms, comprising about 30,000 acres, many makes of tractors, both steam and gas, have been used during the past 10 years, but . . . dependence is being placed more and more on horses. . . . Even on the Cameron Farm, with 18,000 acres under cultivation, steam tractors are used only to help out with plowing and occasionally with discing. We hope in the near future to further restrict their use that they will be used only for threshing."

Another who distinguished himself with success in driving big horse-outfits was E. C. Hallman, of Acadia Valley, Alberta. (*Grain Growers' Guide*, March 19, 1924.) His fame reached far into the United States where he was honored by being named from the office of Secretary of Agriculture as the Best Farm Manager on the continent. He had settled in the area in 1910, and when neighbors were abandoning farms because of drought and poor yields, he was searching for ways to overcome the drought problem and reduce the cost of production.

"Never drive less than twelve horses at one time," E. C. Hallman advised. "It is just as easy to drive twelve horses properly hitched as it is to drive a pair."

In a demonstration for United States visitors, he brought a store clerk who had never driven horses at any time and, after some brief instructions, had him hitch twelve horses and drive them away with a field cultivator. Hallman concentrated on simplification of everything connected with his horses. He used bits on halters instead of bridles, and taking an idea from the organization of a horse-equipped firehall, he widened the stable doors to allow his teams—four horses abreast—to drive right in. From the passage floor, the harness was drawn up on ropes to be suspended from the ceiling until harnessing time in the morning, when the process was reversed. Instead of taking horses back to the stables at noon, he fed from racks fitted with sliding troughs. And while using his work animals so efficiently, he was raising about forty foals per year and feeling no hardship because of depreciation or obsolescence.

A belated effort to improve efficiency of farm horses served to delay the advancing forces of mechanization but not to halt them. The new ideas in horse husbandry were well received as long as the postwar recession lasted. But the economic recession did not last long, and the new farm tractors with greater versatility and reliability began a drive for new heights of popularity.

Chapter 25

Horses Called Back for Service

ISAAC BEATTIE SAID, "As a fine-weather helper, the farm tractor shows up magnificently, but when the going is tough, you need Percherons." In the troubled times of the 1930's, when the old horseman was speaking, the pronouncement sounded most convincing. The "iron horses" with expensive appetites and need for costly repairs were being sentenced to implement shed banishment, temporarily at least. Isaac Beattie was right; they were relatively unreliable. Either soft ground or hard times created circumstances with which the tractors could not cope. There was a minimum of the soft ground caused by surface water in the thirties but when drought and economic depression, working together as members of an evil team, settled over the countryside to linger for most of a decade, tractor sales fell away abruptly, almost reaching the vanishing point.

Until depression struck like an avalanche, business had been booming. People seemed prosperous, and clouds appearing on the business horizon went unnoticed until the failure of a few big international companies triggered a wave of selling on leading stock markets. October 29, 1929, was "Black Friday," and the huge volume of frantic selling on the New York Stock Exchange was said to represent losses of about nine billion dollars. Officials tried to restore confidence with statesments of assurance of early improvement. They urged the public to buy stocks rather than sell. But instead of recovering, market conditions became steadily worse and farm prices followed industrial prices downward to unprecedented depths of disaster. Although the situation was most acute in the Canadian Midwest, the economic plight was international in scope and many overseas countries aggravated it by raising tariffs to protect their own producers.

Wheat prices plunged to ruinous levels, reaching about 50 cents per bushel, basis No. 1 Northern, Fort William, late in 1930, and 38 cents per bushel on December 16, 1932. Translated to prices at country points in Alberta, it meant about 20 cents a bushel for much of the wheat farmers had to sell. Thus, a 60-bushel load of wheat of good grade might bring a total of $12, not much more than the cost of threshing it and hauling it to the country elevator. It was the lowest price for bread wheat in the Canadian record.

Wheat Pools, six years old when the financial panic struck, were in serious trouble, having been overly optimistic in making an initial payment of $1 per bushel on the 1929 crop. Overpayment in Saskatchewan alone amounted to thirteen million dollars. Pressed by the banks which advanced the money, the Pool executives turned to the Provincial Governments for guarantees and loans.

Gloom became as dense as the prairie dust storms. Men in business and government said again that recovery was "just around the corner." But the corner was still far away and many western farmers were unable to pay cash for even the necessities like food. Carloads of fruit and vegetables were shipped as gifts from other provinces. Atlantic coast fishermen, having their own troubles to sell their stocks, sent carload after carload of salt codfish. Farmers receiving these hard slabs of salted fish from well-meaning Maritimers were known to use them for repairing shingled roofs. But farmer determination to cling to independence was most commendable, and pioneer resourcefulness was much in evidence.

Clothing was repaired and garments were made from flour bags and materials which would normally be waste. Farmers traveled long distances to cut wood or dig coal for their stoves. Farm women, determined to be clean even though they could not be prosperous, made soap from unsalable fat. When feed crops failed and livestock population declined, some farm families obtained the only meat for their tables by snaring rabbits and gophers. When asked if members of her family did not grow tired of eating rabbit meat day after day, one resourceful farm woman replied: "No, I've learned twelve different ways of cooking it."

By roasting wheat in the oven of the kitchen range, some women made a coffee substitute, and by using horses instead of tractors, the farm-raised oats and hay became substitutes for gasoline and lubricating oil.

It was a case of sheer necessity. An Alberta farmer who

Anyone who lived during the depression will recognize the Bennett buggy, a familiar mode of transportation on the Prairies during those lean years. When money for gasoline and repairs was not available, farmers brought their horses and even oxen back into service, creating a startling contrast of old and new.

sold a 56-bushel load of wheat on which there were deductions due to the presence of weeds and smut, received a cash ticket for the munificent sum of $3.02. After paying 4½ cents per bushel for threshing, he had a balance of 50 cents, slightly less than 1 cent per bushel for his 56-bushel load. At about the same time, one of his neighbors sold 40 head of cattle and after paying freight and selling commission, had exactly $40 or $1 per head. Another grower shipped 6 cows which graded "canner" and received a settlement of only a fraction of a cent per pound, insufficient to pay for trucking and handling; unable to make up the deficit in cash, the honest farmer gave the trucker another cow.

A trading company received a letter from a customer saying: "You have forwarded my account. I knew I owed you money and I intended to pay. But you will have to wait until I have it. If this was the Day of Judgment and you were no more prepared to face the final test than I am to pay your account, you would just have to go to hell. I am afraid this is all I can offer you at this time."

It was the spirit of the thirties, tragic and yet not without humor. But how, under the circumstances of those years, could any practical farmer think of paying 30 cents a gallon for gasoline? It was bad enough to be paying $1.50 for a pair of new overalls when the old ones ceased to be respectable, or $1.75 for a 100 pounds of flour. People thought in terms of essentials. Food and clothing were essentials to be bought or accepted as gifts from benevolent Canadians in other provinces. Gasoline was not an essential for anybody who still had horses or could get horses.

Those horses which had been turned out—virtually abandoned—to forage for themselves through winter and summer were now rounded up and fitted to such old harness and old horse machinery as could be found and restored for use. When horse implements were not available, tractor plows and other tractor implements were studied to determine the number of horses needed to pull them.

It was hard on horses, many of which had grown soft from inactivity. Their numbers were lower than in the previous years, reflecting the smaller number of mares being bred and foals raised. And the horses remaining on farms averaged older in years. Fortunately, however, there were still enough horses in the country to perform most of the essential operations and farmers turned to them readily, almost instinctively.

Tractor sales, which had been high during the last years of World War I, lagged for a period of postwar adjustment, then flourished, and with the depression, dropped dramatically. Canadian imports of farm tractors in 1929 reached 21,777—with fully two-thirds of all sales being made

Horses were called back to service (top).

Another Bennett buggy (bottom).

Canada Department of Agriculture Photo

in western provinces—and then fell away rapidly as hard times following the economic collapse of that year tightened their grip and brought privation and hardship. Tractors imported for the Canadian trade fell from the figure of 21,777 in 1929, to 5,479 in 1931, and then to a mere 136 in 1933.

Manufacturers and dealers knew the nub of the trade problem was in the farmers' loss of purchasing power. Not only had wheat prices fallen to twenty cents at many country points but prairie farmers had little or nothing to sell. Saskatchewan's wheat crop of 1937 averaged a paltry two and one-half bushels per acre, which meant that most growers had nothing to sell. And other agricultural commodities were similarly low in both volume of production and price offered. Farmers facing feed shortages were obliged to liquidate breeding herds and thereby lost their producing potential. And steers selling for two cents a pound on the hoof and eggs bringing six cents a dozen in trade did nothing to disperse the gloom. Returns from the sale of such commodities left nothing for the purchase of tractors and not much for fuel and repairs.

Resourceful farmers knew they could find horse feed, somewhere, and they could make repairs for harness. Horses offered the only hope. Although a little older and a little fatter from inactivity, most horses could still do a good day's work and it was perfectly logical to call them back to service. Then the problem was in finding men to drive them. Young people who had been operating Titans, Fordsons, and Waterloo Boys were unfamiliar with horse harness, but their elders remembered and were quick to embrace their faithful friends of other years.

Harness had deteriorated; it had become dry and brittle and required to be reconditioned with neatsfoot oil. At the same time, many old two-furrow gang plows had to have their neglected moldboards scoured to rid them of their rust. Tractors on farms were qualifying for a prolonged holiday and tractors resting in dealers' yards looked more and more like derelicts. The "Age of Horses" had returned, and speakers at annual meetings of the horse breeders' associations said, pompously: "We told you so. You can't rely on tractors. Now, never again make the mistake of turning your backs on horses."

Just as horse machinery of an earlier period was adapted with special hitches for use with the new tractors, so in 1932, many three-furrow tractor plows and similar implements were being fitted out with eight-horse eveners and kept in service.

If men on the land could not afford gasoline for tractors, how could they purchase fuel for farm automobiles? The fact was that they could not afford to keep their cars operating. Many farm cars suffered exactly the same fate as that which befell the tractors, although some of the automobiles were revamped to become horse-drawn vehicles and remained on the road. The conversion was not difficult. It was simply a matter of removing the motor and attaching a wagon tongue with a pair of whiffletrees. Buggies and democrats common in the earlier years had largely disintegrated, and these horse-drawn automobiles, known as Bennett buggies, took their places with at least one obvious advantage, soft cushions. Riding on rubber tires, these inventions of the depression years afforded all the riding comfort of the automobile but nothing faster than the speed of the homesteaders' horses and buggies. Symbolizing the depression years on the Canadian Prairies, these strange vehicles were doubtful compliments to the Hon. R. B. Bennett, whose misfortune was to have had the difficult depression years as a time to be Prime Minister of Canada.

The pertinent point was that farm horses had returned from retirement to serve in much the same manner as in pioneer years. For how long would they be back in harness? Opinions differed, just as the views of horsemen and tractor men had always differed. But a few thoughtful people had the correct answer: For as long as the depression lasted.

Chapter 26

Like a Negotiated Peace

WITH THE ONSET OF WORLD WAR II, western agriculture revived from the most difficult and depressing period of years in its history. Rain clouds dispersed the dust clouds and crops responded. The soil seemed eager to prove that it could still produce the world's finest wheat, and markets reacted as though they wanted to be forgiven for past sins. Farmers would not forget the tribulations of the thirties but were ready, without prejudice, for a fresh start. They were ready to recondition their old tractors and as soon as credit or capital permitted, to buy new ones.

Manufacturers, in the meantime, had not been idle. Even in the period when farm-owned tractors were silent occupants of deserted fence corners, motor efficiency was being improved, and farmers found the new machines to be more reliable and more economical to operate than anything they had experienced previously. Dealers were ready to mount their biggest drive for sales, some of them announcing a willingness to take farm horses in lieu of cash. The tractor interests were aiming at nothing short of supremacy in the grain fields, and men on the land were receptive. Once again, horses were being turned out to rustle their own living and harness was being hung away to age and deteriorate.

The decade following 1941 saw farm mechanization making its most spectacular advances. Canada's farm tractors increased by more than 150 per cent in the ten-year period, while farm-owned trucks increased by 153 per cent and harvester-combines soared in numbers by 375 per cent. Canadians were witnessing an agricultural revolution such as they had not seen before. It was a good time to be in the machine business. Manufacturers began to pay bigger dividends, and dealers painted their homes and bought more expensive automobiles. A farm implement agency or dealership with a good line of tractors looked like the best business enterprise on most western town and village streets.

Again the loyal horsemen were on the defensive, fighting a rear-guard battle for survival. All the confidence they seemed to recover when farmers took to driving Bennett buggies in the thirties was being lost. Now their main concern was to save something for animal power. What hope was there in compromise? Conceding some of the advantages claimed for tractors, those professional horsemen insisted that there were still farm jobs which horses would always do better. For certain kinds of agricultural work, they argued fiercely, their animals would never be displaced. Tractors might triumph for plowing, but horses would everlastingly surpass at hauling feed and manure on mixed farms, doing the necessary roadwork under winter conditions, carrying stock saddles when it was necessary to chase cattle off a mountainside or out of a swamp, and, perchance, in such tasks as haying. Horsemen scoffed at the idea of hay for animal feed being cut and raked and hauled by tractors unable to consume and digest it.

The horses' sphere of greatest usefulness could never be defined accurately, the breeders were saying, and for that reason, farmers should never be without them. For the same reason, competition between horses and tractors might continue indefinitely. Perhaps that would be all right too.

Certainly, the best the wise horsemen could see in their future was a working partnership between horses and tractors, especially on those farms big enough to support both kinds of power. It made sense. Many farmers who were quite enthusiastic about mechanical power were still not ready to entrust their fortunes entirely to tractors and oil companies. They liked the convenience offered by tractors and had growing confidence in their economy, but they had seen tractors become useless and hideous when farmers could not buy gasoline and repairs. And with

During the 1940's, farm mechanization made its most spectacular advances. But even with efficient rigs like the one shown here, horsemen were still arguing that for certain kinds of agricultural work, the horse would never be replaced.

Leonard A. Hillyard Photo

memories of war, they asked: "What if the machine factories and oil refineries were bombed?" Without some horses and harness to fall back upon, farm work could be paralyzed. Sure, the farmers were saying, they would buy tractors but they were not ready for the risk of operating totally without horses. The working partnership looked well; it would allow tractors to do most of the heavy work like plowing and leave the horses to do the drilling, haying, hauling, and winter chores where livestock required attention.

Of course, there were many factors to be considered in choosing farm power—farm topography, soil, feed costs, and the farmer's individual preferences, for example. But such factors were not likely to change the case for the partnership arrangement, which was receiving the endorsation of extension workers and farm editors.

"Many farmers are beginning to find out that it is no longer a question of horse or tractor, but a question of horse and tractor," noted one of those editors, trying to adhere to a moderate line and still hold the loyalty of people with sentiment for horses. "What combination of horse and tractor power will provide the most economical power, provide the greatest concentration for seasonal demands and insure the most scientific preparation of the soil for ensuing crops? On the majority of farms of over half a section in extent, neither animal nor motor power will serve all these ends alone. On every one of these farms there is a happy combination which would give the maximum profit per acre or per laborer."

It was becoming more and more popular to talk about horses and tractors sharing the burden of farm power. Guest speakers from the universities or departments of agriculture reminded their audiences that farmers having access to the two forms of power and thus able to shift the main load even slightly from one to the other would always enjoy added security.

Representatives of the machine companies, with the tide of events flowing strongly in their favor, were not eager to accept compromise, but the organized horsemen, seeing an opportunity to save at least part of their crumbling industry, gave faint endorsation to the new idea by proclaiming for the principle: "At least one four-horse team of drafters on every farm."

For the horsemen, it bore some resemblance to a "negotiated peace" but it did not bring the stabilization they expected. The makers and dealers in tractors had no intention of limiting their efforts and output. Time was working in their favor and they knew it. Forces which caused agriculture to flourish during the years of World War I were again at work. Farmers were enjoying the return of markets, they could obtain capital for the purchase of equipment, they were desperately short of help; and tractors offered the best solutions for their problems. The buying rush began again, with the most exciting chapters in farm mechanization being written in the prairie region.

It was the adoption of tractors, of course, that led to the other notable advances in mechanization. For all of Canada, tractor numbers rose from a mere 6 per 100 farms in 1921, to 14 per 100 farms in 1931, then 22 per 100 farms in 1941, and 64 per 100 farms in 1951. In the latter year, 70 per cent of all the tractors in Canada were in the three midwestern provinces, with the total number in the area almost equaling the total number of farms. For that three-province area, there were 13 farm tractors per 100 farms in 1921, 29 per 100 farms in 1931, 38 per 100 farms in 1941, and 95 per 100 farms in 1951.

Now, regardless of sentiment, the farming country had too many horses, and something had to be done about them.

Chapter 27

"Horsemeat and Gravy"

THE IMPACT OF THOUSANDS of new tractors extended far. Implement dealers gained wealth and prestige, while harness merchants went out of business, and veterinarians saw their profession slump. The most crucial adjustments, of course, were right on the farms. Every time a man on the land bought a new tractor, from two to six draft horses qualified to be retired and turned out to forage for their living.

Saskatchewan, which had a million horses in 1921, could still count 800,000 in 1941, many of them old and many unlikely to be harnessed again. Fully a quarter of a million of them were considered surplus. What was to be done with them? The circumstances of war emphasized the folly of keeping unproductive animals. Farmers and ranchers were being urged to produce more beef for domestic and United Kingdom needs, and beef prices were rising steadily. Why allow unproductive horses to eat grass which could be used with profit by cattle? That question suggested another. If the ranges were to be cleared for more cattle, what could be done with the surplus horse stock?

A few old horses were regularly sold to furnish meat for fur farms, but neither the small number involved nor the price of five to ten dollars per head made the trade seem important. Some other horses suitable for work in the lumber woods and on farms were shipped to eastern Canadian markets but this movement, like the sales to fox farms, made but slight impression upon the thousands of head running on the western grasslands. A proposal to destroy a few hundred thousand of the inferior animals by the simple expedient of shooting was not well received because such a plan would be wasteful, also repulsive to people who retained a sense of indebtedness to animals which had served so faithfully in earlier years. Surely there was some better way of effecting the desired adjustment in the power resources of the West.

While much was being heard about the rising famine in war-torn countries of Europe, it could not be overlooked that meat from thousands of western horses could be the means of saving lives and relieving a serious crisis. Differing from Canadians, the people in many of the overseas countries fighting malnutrition were accustomed to eating horsemeat and would be sure to welcome shipments of it.

The proposal to process horsemeat and sell it in Europe was discussed widely in 1943, and in the autumn of that year, as demand for meats, leather, glue, and other animal products was reaching record proportions, the department of animal husbandry at the University of Saskatchewan conducted cutting tests on horse carcasses and not only provided useful data about yields and values but led some unsuspecting consumers to say: "That's excellent meat but it does seem to have an unusual flavor for beef."

More and more stockmen were coming to the view that they should be doing something for themselves in this matter of correcting horse numbers. A meeting was held at Val Marie, in southwestern Saskatchewan, on March 1, 1944, and the 300 farmers and ranchers who attended made it very clear that they wanted an action program. They agreed with a suggestion to organize co-operatively and examine all the possible outlets for horses. In the weeks following, local meetings were held, with L. B. Thomson, superintendent of the Swift Current Experimental Farm, attending and acting as chairman at each. Late in the same month, a general meeting was held at Swift Current and a provisional board was appointed. George Newton, of Val Marie, was elected provisional chairman and L. B. Thomson, secretary. Mr. Thomson was then instructed to go to the United States for the purpose of studying possible markets there.

Reporting a few weeks later, Mr. Thomson proposed "a horse-killing plant at a central point," as a first step in preparing for the export of horsemeat. It was common knowledge that European countries would need and want meat foods in all available forms so horsemen should be ready with something to sell, even though the starting of a co-operative abattoir would be attended by considerable risk. Capital would be needed, also experience.

Organization progressed rapidly, but the infant association was greatly handicapped for funds. At a meeting in December of 1944, it was reported that the big program was at that time backed by a cash balance of exactly $63.93. But there was vigor even though there was not much cash, and before the end of the year, the provisional board was invited by the Saskatchewan Government to accept backing for a loan of $50,000 for the purpose of starting a plant in which to process horsemeat.

The horsemen were in business, and in May, 1945, with the aid of the Federal Government, a contract was signed to deliver, starting in the following September, 10,000 tons of pickled horsemeat to Belgium. Obviously, an abattoir was an immediate need, and steps were taken at once to buy an old power plant at Swift Current and renovate it. The next move was to purchase the Red Top slaughtering plant at Edmonton. The co-operative's members were "going to succeed or go broke trying." When the first annual meeting was held on June 9, 1945, only the Edmonton plant was in production but L. B. Thomson was elected president and S. F. Shields was elected secretary, and organizers and members were told to expect new and bigger contracts for horsemeat products.

At the war's end it became clear that European countries wanted meat in cans. A canning plant would be costly and the co-operative had nothing but borrowed money and all of it appropriated for other purposes. One way or another, however, the money needed to install the canning operation was obtained. The Belgium Economic Mission advanced $150,000 on meat to be delivered later. The Saskatchewan Government increased its guarantee to a similar amount, and later, when the United Nations Relief and Rehabilitation Administration (UNRRA) contracted to take the entire 1946 output, there was another advance of $200,000.

The Swift Current plant began to operate on October 19, 1945. The risks of failure were still evident and most members realized it. But by the beginning of 1946, the co-operative was beginning to appear as a robust and expanding enterprise. Horse supplies were available in abundance, and meat and meat products were wanted most urgently by overseas agencies. Optimistic members were subscribing to a one-dollar share in the association for each horse delivered and, at the same time, agreeing to a three-dollar deduction from the proceeds of each horse to provide working capital and additional equipment.

By the end of 1947, over 100,000 horses had been processed in the two plants, and producers had been paid about $3,000,000 in cash. But the co-operative's troubles were not all in the past. The year 1948 brought reverses. The UNRRA contract was canceled because of the operation of the Marshall Plan, and at the end of the year the horsemen's organization had over 400,000 pounds of canned meat on hand and no visible market. Both 1948 and 1949 were years of loss, and 1950 and 1951 were difficult. The overseas' demand had changed completely, but strangely enough, a measurable demand for horsemeat appeared in Canada. Most native-born Canadians wanted no part in the eating of horsemeat; but beef prices were higher than they had ever been, and there was sufficient interest in horsemeat from New Canadians that horsemeat stores were opened in most cities. But the existence of the horsemeat stores was brief. Of thirty-three shops licensed to sell horsemeat in Winnipeg and points west of there in 1951, most of them were still operating in 1952 but only three were licensed in 1953.

Even though the big export market disappeared, the co-operative had served its purpose and the two plants were offered for sale. Instead of being sold immediately, however, the plants were leased for three years, and on June 30, 1955, when the lease expired, the leasing company bought both. The Horse Marketing Association was then in a position to wind up its business affairs. Notices were mailed to 37,000 shareholders notifying them of district meetings expected to be the last. And the final report could tell of processing almost a quarter of a million surplus horses and their conversion to $19,000,000 worth of products. The long list of sales included 56,000,000 pounds of "canned horsemeat and gravy," 196,000 pounds of canned "luncheon" meat, 6,500 tons of pickled horsemeat, 3,600,000 pounds of "domestic horsemeat," 10,000,000 pounds of frozen hinds and fronts, 18,500 tons of meat for fur-farm trade, and the usual range of byproducts like hair, hides, and fats.

It was a strange list of products to be associated with Canadian horsemen, and at least a few of the older horsemen, for reasons of sentiment, refused to discuss it. To them, the farmers' "friends" through the pioneer years deserved a better retirement. But the project had served its purpose, which had been to create an outlet for many of those horses that had become a burden on farms and ranches rapidly swinging to mechanization. It was a bold adventure in co-operative marketing, carried through with the courage and the resourcefulness typical of the horsemen who guided it. And in addition to leaving the ranges with fewer of the unwanted animals, the program left the agricultural West more completely in the grip of tractor power.

Chapter 28

More Power, More Comfort, More Debt

AN ALBERTA FARMER taking delivery of a 1970-model tractor was heard to remark that he would now command "more field power, more working comfort and convenience and more debt" than at any time in his farming career. The new and sophisticated thing, rated at 135 horsepower, would pull up to eight plows and was described as a turbocharged diesel. It had eight forward speeds ranging to eighteen miles per hour, and two reverse speeds. It had a six-cylinder high-compression motor, power steering, dual headlights, a twelve-position adjustable seat for the driver, and a cab offering "livingroom comfort with sundeck view." For what more could a power farmer ask, unless it were a price which would be somewhat less than the equivalent of a quarter section of wheat land?

It was a bigger tractor than most of those seen on farms, but the fact was that the popular fancy in tractor size was changing again. Older farmers remembered when all tractors were massive, awkward, and slow. But the big ones lost favor and demand was for small ones. After more years, farmers were asking for bigger tractors to match their bigger farms, and the popular unit came to have the appearance of a tractor of medium size and the power of a big one. The sixty-five tractors tested in the University of Nebraska Tractor Testing Lab in 1920 averaged 33½ in horsepower; and the thirty-two tractors tested in 1968 averaged over 70 horsepower.

When the Canadian Western Farm and Ranch Show was held at Edmonton in March, 1970, each manufacturer had an opportunity to display one unit from its line of tractors. Except for a few garden-type tractors, almost all the models elected for display carried ratings of 100 horsepower or over. One giant machine, with four-wheel drive and a rating of 169 horsepower, would have had no place on any but a very big farm. But western farms were becoming bigger, and their operators, quite obviously, wanted bigger tractors.

Tractor change was so great that even the most popular designs of 1926 appeared as antiques in 1966. Thanks to testing programs and the growing responsibility of manufacturers eager to gain the image of reliability, most changes were along sound and progressive lines. Farmers bought even the newest types with confidence such as they could not have found in earlier years. Some of that confidence was attributable to assurances coming from tractor-testing services conducted at Nebraska from 1919. A Waterloo Boy carried the tag of "Test Number One," and on December 2, 1968, Nebraska "Test Number 1,000" was conducted on a very modern diesel. In the intervening years, other states and provinces heard proposals for the establishment of local tractor-testing facilities, but as pointed out on various occasions by Prof. J. MacGregor Smith of the University of Saskatchewan and the University of Alberta, there was no particular advantage in duplicating what was being done—and done well—at Nebraska.

Some of the changes and improvements making farm tractors more efficient and more convenient—as well as more costly—should be noted. Self-starters, demonstrated about 1920, were adopted in the 1930's, sparing operators the tiring necessity of cranking by hand and the arm-breaking consequence of backfiring.

The newest feature of 1926 was the power take-off, allowing power from the motor to be transmitted to binder or mower or other implement without the necessity of keeping the tractor in motion. As in the case of front-end and rear-end mounted implements, the effect was to extend tractor usefulness.

One of the most notable changes came with the almost universal adoption of pneumatic tires for wheel-drive tractors. Allis-Chalmers placed those rubber tires on tractors in 1932, and in a surprisingly short time, other companies followed and the old steel-mounted machines with heavy angle-iron cleats disappeared. With benefit of rubber, tractors could find added traction and be driven at much higher road speeds. The two-mile-an-hour speed of the heavy tractors in pioneer years would seem like monotony along-

Preparing the seedbed.

Seeding on a one-tractor farm.

Seeding with modern equipment.

T. R. Melville-Ness Photos

side a modern mounted-on-rubber model moving fast enough to break the village speed limit.

Many of the changes were to make the operator's work load lighter and his entire effort more effective, as in the mechanical aids in handling tractor machinery. When plowing with a heavy tractor in 1915, plows were raised and lowered individually by means of levers and every gang of tractor plows required the attention of a full-time attendant. But with the coming of small tractors, mechanical lifts replaced hand levers and then hydraulic lifts were adopted. The tractor operator's control board became more sophisticated, just as his cab became more attractive and his tractor seat more comfortable.

It was natural that the new tractor with a wider range of capabilities would be found performing an ever-greater number of farm tasks and chores. Whereas the early types were largely restricted to plowing and heavy belt work, the new ones were used for all kinds of field work, all jobs in the hayfields, clearing of brushland, building roads, pulling and topping sugar beets, lifting and hauling manure, moving snow, digging postholes, and even for stretching fence wire. Versatility was the new characteristic in farming communities from which draft horses had virtually disappeared.

That mechanization of agriculture advanced faster and farther in the prairie region than in any other part of Canada did not surprise anybody. The farms there were bigger, and the manner of farming invited heavier equipment and bigger risks.

If there was such a thing as an average census farm in Manitoba, Saskatchewan, and Alberta in 1966, it was one comprising 685 acres, 437 acres of which were "improved," meaning that they were producing domestic crops or in summerfallow. At the time of the official count, June 1, that farm had 36 head of cattle, 11 pigs, 2 sheep, 118 poultry and 1 horse which, it might be assumed, conformed to saddle type more than to draft. Compared with an average census farm in the six eastern provinces, the western unit was four times as large in acreage, carried twice as many cattle, had fewer pigs and poultry and had a much bigger investment in tractors and other machinery. (Compiled from *Canada Year Book* data.)

Many western farmers admitted that power machinery had become an obsession. Across their three provinces there were 160 tractors for every 100 farms, 115 motor trucks per 100 farms, and 69 grain combines per 100 farms. The capital investment in machinery and equipment averaged $11,219, over 20 per cent of the total capital investment of $55,862. The eastern farm had become mechanized also, and considered on the basis of tractors per 100-acre or more farms rather than per 100 farms, it was highly mechanized. The 1966 census figures for those eastern

Combining on a big modern farm.
T. R. Melville-Ness Photo

provinces showed 122 tractors per 100 farms, 49 motor trucks, and 16 grain combines, while the average capital investment in machinery and equipment per census farm was $5,738 or about 17 per cent of the total. Clearly, the Canadian farmer had become an esteemed customer of the machine companies and the western farmer, with bigger holdings, an especially-esteemed customer whose fortunes in the marketing of produce was a prime factor in determining company dividends.

Farm tractor replacement averaged about 10 per cent per year, but when crops or markets failed, farmers bought more repairs and fewer new tractors and manufacturers prepared for reduced sales and reduced profits. Company officials followed the movement of wheat, knowing it was likely to be the biggest single factor in determining volume of business for them. When Canada's grain exports were falling in recent years, makers and dealers in machinery knew what to expect: Sales of all farm implements and repairs dropped from $494,298,000 in 1967 to $406,646,000 in 1969.

The whole Canadian economy felt the impact from new tractors in large numbers, but the most massive impact was upon the shape and character of agriculture itself. Farms increased in size and a greater number of farm homes stood abandoned. With the new mechanical power, fewer operators and workers were needed and rural population declined. One man with the newest power machinery could work several times as much land as could his father or his grandfather using the equipment available to them.

George Lane of the Bar U Ranch, in 1908, had eighty horses and twenty-eight hired men to farm the land which Senator Harry Hays ultimately worked with three men and the best modern tractor power. And, according to the Senator, "we now produce about twice as much on the same ground." While a farm worker in the World War II period produced roughly enough food for himself and ten other human consumers, his modern counterpart, employing the most up-to-date machinery aids, can produce enough for himself and about twenty others.

Farmers argued that the tractors they wanted should not cost them as much as they were required to pay, and a government-appointed commission agreed. But they bought just the same, and there was no doubt about the new machines increasing the effectiveness and output of each worker and making it possible for rural people to enjoy more of the rewards of leisure. Because production costs were beaten to near-minimum and farms were made more productive, standards of living were raised appreciably. The gap between rural and urban living was made more narrow. It would have been difficult for even an old and loyal horseman to deny the gains.

Chapter 29

A Home for Old Tractors

A PIONEER WHO KNEW all about the steam and gasoline tractors that displaced oxen and horses, remarked. "If old machines could talk, they'd tell some of the damnedest stories you ever heard." And later, when visiting the Western Development Museum at Saskatoon during the week of the annual Pion-Era program, the elderly gentleman heard many of the old things "talking" and his face brightened, reflecting the rekindling of latent affections. He saw women making butter with dash churns, men threshing grain with the loosely-jointed flails, oxen pulling walking-plows and displaying typical disdain for the job, horses traveling in labored circles to drive power sweeps, animals working treadmills and performing various field jobs, gas buggies giving hint of the coming age of automobiles, and tractors with fantastic designs pulling farm implements.

There was the hand-hewn Red River cart, which had carried freight over the long prairie trails in pre-rail years. There was the 1907 Russell touring car, made in Canada and bought and driven by Fred Green, of the Moose Jaw district. There was the huge custom-built Peerless automobile of 1910, ordered by Senator James Lougheed, of Calgary, at a reported price of $13,000 and then acquired by Frank Collicutt, of Hereford cattle fame. There was the 40,000-pound, 110-horsepower Case steamer, bought in 1912 by Langley Brothers, of Richard, Saskatchewan, and used for plowing with a twelve-furrow gang and threshing with one of the biggest separators available. There were hundreds of heavy attractions and to outclass them all was the proud old Reeves steamer rated at 32-120 horsepower, which Curator George Shepherd called the "Grand Old Lady of the Fleet," actually pulling a twenty-furrow gang of plows and purring gently as if the load did not worry her in the least.

Until a country reaches a certain stage of maturity, its history, traditions, and relics are likely to receive less attention than they deserve and many treasures handed down from the past may become lost. It happened too often in the Canadian West that the rich stories from frontier years were allowed to be forgotten before they were set to record, and the tools and implements were allowed to be sold and shipped away as junk. Old buggies disintegrated; old churns ended their days on scrap piles, and old tractors were taken away by dealers in scrap metal. Thus, many of the long, evolutionary lines connecting reapers with combines, for example, and primitive tractors with the most modern types, were permanently broken.

But, happily, not all the links in the chain of agricultural implements became lost. While many valuable specimens could still be located, a few thoughtful citizens around North Battleford, Saskatoon, and elsewhere took steps to gather and save as much as possible. They saw clearly that unless a program of recovery was undertaken without more delay, many machines and implements of the frontier period would be lost as surely and completely as the passenger pigeons were lost.

At the end of World War II, the years of which had seen thousands of old tractors sold for scrap iron, the importance of saving representative specimens came up for discussion at the Battleford Historical Society. Frank Swan, member and pioneer farmer, urged the establishment of a museum for the housing and the display of agricultural machines used in frontier years. The proposal was presented to J. L. Phelps, at that time Minister of Natural Resources in the Saskatchewan Government. He reacted with instant enthusiasm. He, too, had expressed concern about the loss of rare old machines and had acquired some heavy pieces to save them from destruction for scrap. The Minister placed a proposal to assemble museum pieces before his government colleagues and obtained their

Stan Reynolds, founder and owner of Stan Reynolds Museum in Wetaskiwin, Alberta, inspects a Sawyer-Massey 11-22 horsepower tractor prior to moving it to the museum (top).

Don Carrothers, of Austin, Manitoba (bottom), was demonstrating his old Case 22-65 steamer as far back as 1949. That was the beginning of an idea which he nursed into the thriving and active Agricultural Memorial Museum of Manitoba at Austin, now holding an imposing collection of ancient tractors.

approval and authorization for financial assistance. Without delay, a campaign was started for the purpose of locating and preserving the most significant of these agricultural tools overlooked by dealers still combing the country for scrap iron. Mr. Phelps continued to give much personal attention to the program and a big part of the success which followed was due to his exceptional energy.

By a special act of 1949, the Legislature of Saskatchewan established the Western Development Museum and provided for a Board of Directors to be appointed by the Lieutenant-Governor in Council. One of the first tasks of the new board was in finding accommodation for the acquired articles. Premises would have to be spacious, and the needed accommodation was secured by leasing or buying air force hangars no longer in use by the Commonwealth Air Training Plan. Saskatoon, to which point a large hangar was moved amid unusual difficulties, became the administrative and repair center and skilled workmen were engaged to make repairs. Other museums were stocked and opened at North Battleford and Yorkton.

Small things like spinning wheels, washtubs, and flintlock guns were not overlooked, and the museum catalogue grew to include more than 10,000 items. But those small articles could be found in conventional museums, and the new emphasis was to be on heavy equipment like road vehicles,

Joe Phelps, Saskatchewan farmer and former cabinet minister in the Provincial Government. His efforts and enthusiasm did much to bring the Western Development Museum to international distinction.

field implements, and farm tractors in all their strange glory. Nothing was to capture the interest of visitors to the new Western Development Museum like the long rows of tractor relics, many of them appearing as the giants of the mechanical world.

It became museum policy to restore the old machines to working order whenever that was possible. Having them in running condition enhanced their educational and inspirational value, and visitors present for Pion-Era programs had the opportunity to see as many as fourteen different makes and models of the slow-moving steam tractors—dinosaurs of the mechanical evolution—traveling under their own power at one time. It was enough to make the earth tremble, and visitors had good reason to exclaim: "Where else in the world could a person see such a display?" Valued at several millions of dollars, the museum treasure has been described as the biggest and best collection of agricultural machinery in existence. It is a fitting dedication to the memory of the men and the women who pioneered on the Canadian Great Plains and nearby Parkbelts.

The annual Pion-Era, when hundreds of the old exhibits at the Western Development Museum "come to life" to delight local people and visitors, was in the nature of an Open House and became a national attraction. Better than anywhere else, the Saskatoon Pion-Era succeeded in presenting scenes and cultures from homestead years, demonstrating the agricultural machines which opened the West, and in reviving many of the bitter debates about the merits of tractor power, and many vivid memories of big threshing outfits, harvesters' excursions, burning strawpiles illuminating the night like giant candles, and the coming of combines to completely change the character of harvest operations.

But the Western Development Museum was not alone in capturing and preserving Western Canada's agricultural relics. Private efforts in each of the Prairie Provinces met with success.

As far back as 1949 Don Carrothers, of Austin, Manitoba, fired up his Case 22-65 steamer and showed it off at Portage la Prairie. It was the beginning of an idea and with the added enthusiasm of Ben Richardson, of Bagot, Manitoba, who was interested in the smaller historical items, the idea grew. Now a thriving and active museum, the Agricultural Memorial Museum of Manitoba at Austin is supported by people and communities for miles around and attended by thousands during the annual Threshermen's Reunion, usually held early in August, when an imposing collection of ancient tractors is displayed.

In Alberta, what is recognized as the largest collection of privately-owned tractors and other machines is at Wetaskiwin where Stan Reynolds, with a business background in implement and automobile dealerships, was able to present the museum with the results of many years of searching and assembling. As one of the first people to recognize an urgency in recovering and safeguarding the surviving machines, he was scouring the countryside long before he had any thought of a museum with an appeal for tourists. In gaining possession of the large implements like steam tractors, he was often "just two steps ahead of the junk dealers."

When the Wetaskiwin collection achieved large proportions, its owner realized the necessity of providing appropriate building accommodation and proceeded to construct a museum building, 60 feet by 128 feet, on the west side of the Number 2 Highway of 1956. Thereafter, the costly work of repairing machines and preparing them for presentation to the public was pursued with greater vigor than ever.

Nothing succeeds like success and when the proprietor's determination to safeguard those machinery links with pioneer years was recognized, numerous other machines deserving museum space were brought to his attention. Some of these were purchased; some were accepted as gifts, and some were taken on a sort of "lend-lease" basis. In all cases, there were problems of transportation and reconditioning. When missing parts could not be purchased

For years steamers were the biggest, the strongest and the steadiest sources of power for farm fields, and they had a loyal following. Now they can be seen steaming again at pioneer and agricultural museums.

Alberta Archives Photo

through the established channels, they had to be made. Sometimes, two old specimens of the same make and model were found, and from them one typical and workable machine was reconstructed—the only way by which the purpose could have been achieved.

A lumbering old steam tractor weighing twenty tons could not be regarded as an easy-to-handle museum piece, and bringing such monsters out of the soil in which they had settled since their retirement and delivering them to their new home for old engines could present great difficulties.

There was the case of the heavy steamer bearing the date of 1909 and used on a farm west of Edmonton. Hearing about it, Mr. Reynolds hastened to locate the owner, only to learn that a representative of the Western Development Museum had been through the district a few days earlier and bought the antique for $200. As it happened, however, the old tractor had not turned a wheel since bogging down in muskeg some years earlier, and the purchaser was assuming the responsibility of getting it out and loading it for shipment. Extricating the huge tonnage appeared increasingly hopeless to the Saskatchewan purchaser, and Mr. Reynolds, confident of success in recovering the monster, took it off the new owner's hands at the same price and managed to deliver it to Wetaskiwin. It was like an operation in "lifesaving."

Regardless of the museum to which those old tractors and other agricultural machines have been taken, the men who prevented their destruction as scrap performed a valuable public service. Had the recovery been long delayed, hundreds more of those mechanical treasures would have been lost and succeeding generations been denied the opportunity of seeing and studying them.

"Homes For Old Tractors" were provided; "Homes For Old Horses" were suggested from time to time but never realized, for the rather obvious reason that they were not really practical. The Horseman's Hall of Fame at Calgary is a fitting tribute to the pioneer horses and horsemen, but the best that can be accorded those equine slaves of the early years is an acknowledgement of debt to them and a lasting place of respect and affection in the hearts of the men and the women who remember them.

Index

About the Author

Grant MacEwan, well-known Canadian author, has more than 20 books to his credit, written during his varied career as a teacher, administrator, journalist, statesman, and agriculture specialist.

He was born in Manitoba in 1902, but spent most of his early years on the family farm near Melfort, Saskatchewan, where he completed his primary education. This was followed by attendance at the Ontario College of Agriculture at Guelph, from which he graduated with a B.S.A. degree. He did his post-graduate work at Iowa, and then joined the University of Saskatchewan in Saskatoon from 1928-1946. In 1946 he was appointed Dean of Agriculture of the University of Manitoba and he remained in that post until 1951 when he resigned in order to have more time to pursue his many other interests. In that year, Calgary became his home.

During the next ten years he served as alderman, mayor, and then as a member of the Alberta Legislature. In 1965 he was appointed Lieutenant-Governor of Alberta.

Since leaving office in 1974, he has remained active in both public and private life — answering numerous requests for speaking engagements, teaching Western Canadian history at the University of Calgary and at Olds Community College, and working on his farm near Sundre, Alberta.